It's Great To Be Alive

Remembering River Park's Pioneering Addiction Treatment

RIVER PARK ®

By Terry Woster

With a Foreword by
Glenn and Phyllis Jorgenson

ISBN 13: 978-0-615-62570-6

Editor: Kathleen McGreevy, Chapter Savers, LLC
Cover Design: Paula Habbena, Fine Art Studios
Book Design: Linda Coffin, HistoryCrafters

For additional copies, contact:
South Dakota Hall of Fame
1480 South Main Avenue
Chamberlain, South Dakota 57325
(800) 697-3130
www.sdhalloffame.com

Table of Contents

You feel it when you enter.

Not just the physical appearance, which is beautiful, restful and tasteful, but also a kind of aura that envelops you.

At first I thought it was the people who work there. I grant they are special and a very unusual group of individuals. I can tell they do their work with dedication, and what they do is not just a job—but a career of unselfish devotion to a cause that is larger than even their personal desires or ambitions.

But it is not them, nor is it the physical attributes that give River Park the aura of quiet, peaceful consolation.

I know now what it is that brings that comforting sense of security and peace.

It is the clients who come to us and leave us, but who leave behind part of themselves, the sweet part—their gratitude, the spirit balm they found here, the purposeful living of a life of dedication they go forth to live, which they found here in a spiritual awakening, bringing serenity to their lives.

That is the magic of River Park.

—Lloyd Jorgenson (Glenn Jorgenson's father)

Foreword

by Glenn and Phyllis Jorgenson

This is the story of River Park, South Dakota's first privately funded, not-for-profit treatment center for alcoholism.

It describes how, with the help of many, we opened three inpatient treatment centers in our home state—in Pierre (1971), in Rapid City (1981) and in Sioux Falls (1984). It shows how Phyllis led our efforts to meet the needs of family members of alcoholics. It traces the development of River Park's other efforts to treat the disease of alcoholism—community resource centers in eight smaller South Dakota cities, and a workplace employee assistance program.

This story also documents our many efforts to expand understanding about the disease of alcoholism—our newsletters, our booklets, our presentations to civic clubs, schools and church groups across the state, our website (www.riverparksd.com), our display at the South Dakota Hall of Fame—and most of all, our television series featuring celebrities who were affected by alcoholism or other chemical dependencies.

This story includes the 1988 merger of River Park with Parkside Medical Services, a division of the Lutheran General Healthcare System, and the 1992 decision of LHS to close its alcohol treatment facilities in South Dakota.

But Terry Woster, the author of this book, has achieved far more than a recitation of the dates and events found in a conventional history.

By telling the story of his own struggle with alcoholism, and by telling the story of Glenn's similar battle, Terry illuminates the mindset of those who persist in drinking even when it becomes obvious that they are harming themselves and others.

He then shows, step by painstaking step, how the principles of Alcoholics Anonymous—seasoned with a generous dose of respect and love—can help individuals overcome addiction.

That was the core of the River Park philosophy, and it is the most important part of our history.

As we reviewed our history, we were reminded of the thousands of people who contributed to the success of River Park—government leaders, business and community supporters, clergy members, educators, celebrities, medical workers, media personnel, staff members, family members and most importantly, those recovering from alcohol or chemical dependency. Not all of them are named in this book, but our gratitude to all of them is heartfelt.

Now, after four decades of educational programs about alcoholism, we hope this book will continue those educational efforts. Perhaps a new generation of celebrities will decide to draw public attention to the problems of addiction and the need of so many for affordable, effective treatment. Maybe the stories told here will bring a ray of hope to people imprisoned in denial and despair.

We pray that the many still suffering—the afflicted and the affected—will find the way out and learn that "it's great to be alive."

— Glenn and Phyllis Jorgenson
June, 2012

Preface

by
Terry Woster

I visited River Park in Pierre, South Dakota, and met its director, Glenn Jorgenson, for the first time in 1976.

The alcoholism treatment center on the east bank of the Missouri River was in its sixth year, preparing to launch a series of television programs featuring celebrities who sat before a camera and told the world they were recovering alcoholics. I worked for a news service at the time. Jorgenson invited me to a sneak preview of the first few shows of what would become the popular *It's Great To Be Alive* series. If the preview impressed me, he said, maybe I could put together a story for the state wire.

I covered politics, the state Legislature mostly. A story on a bunch of do-gooders and their television series, I could do without. Even so, as a political reporter, I'd learned early in the game to make as many contacts in as many different social, business, economic and philosophical camps as I could. A guy never knew who might be helpful in chasing the next big story.

I'd heard about Jorgenson, of course. He'd been a big shot in state government in the 1960s, and an aggressive businessman and investor all over Pierre, the capital city. Somewhere along the line, he'd run into some kind of trouble, and I'd heard he'd gotten religion. He'd sworn off the booze and started a treatment center. He traveled all over the state, all over the country, for that matter, talking about alcoholism and drug addiction.

Fanatics and true believers didn't do much for me, and the last thing I needed was to spend time with a guy who wanted to talk about not drinking. Still, Jorgenson knew all the movers and shakers in South Dakota. That made him potentially a valuable contact in a business that was all about contacts.

I agreed to view a couple of the shows and talk with Jorgenson a bit. We set the appointment for his office at River Park. He said he'd have sandwiches and coffee and he'd have me in and out of the place in no more than an hour.

Now, I drank pretty regularly at that time in my life. The nature of my job required it. At least, that's what I told myself—and my wife—on those evenings when I'd stumble into the house while she was washing the dishes from a supper I'd missed. A reporter learned a lot in the bars. Tongues loosened with each round of drinks. Secrets spilled out like a double shot of vodka. I couldn't do my job if I didn't hang around with the happy-hour crowd once in a while.

She'd already begun suggesting I had a drinking problem. I knew better.

I got rave reviews from my bosses about my work, after all. The daily newspaper editors who used my stories loved me. At 32, I could drink beer late into the night and still be at work before 8 a.m., ready to tackle the toughest assignment. I made good money, got promotions and commendations. That wasn't the performance of a person with a drinking problem.

Had I known then what I learned in later years, I could have ticked off a dozen danger signals.

I drank for all the wrong reasons, for one thing. Actually, I drank for only one reason, to get high. I drank to get rid of feelings. That's the way it had been from my first drink. I didn't drink in high school. I started on graduation night, splitting a six-pack of beer with two of my best friends. The first drink, although I didn't like the taste of the beer, made me feel better than good. I felt wonderful. I felt important. I felt like a whole different person, not the shy goody-goody who never did anything wrong or made anybody angry.

From that first drink of beer on that warm June evening in 1962, I drank to recapture that feeling.

I drank to excess often. Throughout college my drinking increased and my grades slipped, slowly at first, then like an avalanche. I graduated from high school as class valedictorian. By the time I finished college, my grade point was barely a C-plus. In my last semester at college my transcript showed eight credit hours of "D" work, barely passing my major course of study, journalism. I blamed it on an instructor who had it in for me. I should have blamed it on the beer and whiskey I drank almost daily at the parties I chose over studying.

For years I clutched stubbornly to the belief that a person couldn't have a drinking problem unless he'd had trouble with the law. By trouble with the law, I meant a drunken driving conviction, I guess. Only much later did I connect drinking with a college incident in which I was arrested with four other guys for stealing a dozen Christmas trees. We paid fines to the city and earned a year on social probation from the college. Never once did it occur to me that we probably wouldn't have even thought about taking those trees if we hadn't been sitting around the apartment that Friday night drinking beer after beer and daring each other to do something wild.

Embarrassing as the incident was, I blamed it on the typical hi-jinks a college kid will pull off, not on the drinking that preceded the stupid act of petty larceny. I wasn't alone. My folks, the Dean of Men, the town cop, the magistrate, all of them suggested this kind of prank ought to be stopped. None of them suggested I ought to think about not drinking.

After college, I married and got a newspaper job. We soon had a baby, and even though we both had been working, money was tight. We made friends with a couple in the same condition. Our socializing consisted of popcorn and iced tea, not nights on the town and booze.

Because I didn't drink often for a few years, I used that period later to prove to myself that I didn't need to drink. Much later, after I learned more about alcoholism, I could see that, even during my "dry" periods, drinking remained far too important to me. Whenever I'd get a bonus, whenever we'd have something to celebrate, I'd scrape together enough money for a case of beer or a fifth of inexpensive bourbon.

Drinking dominated my thoughts, whether I actually drank or not.

By the time I reached River Park in 1976, I was drinking often and a lot. I wouldn't have admitted I was an alcoholic, though, not for anything. Not even after I sat with Jorgenson and listened to part of his drinking history. Not even after I watched the preview tapes of his television program and heard actors Garry Moore and Dick Van Dyke call themselves recovering alcoholics and describe drinking patterns not so different from my own.

I left River Park that day thinking what a good place it was "for the sort of folks who need that kind of help." I left believing I still controlled my drinking, although to this day I can remember how a sudden fear gripped me as I walked down the hallway toward the door to the parking lot.

It hit me so hard I could hardly keep walking. I managed to get to my car, though, and I sat for long minutes by myself, breathing hard, trying to make my hand reach to put the key in the ignition.

I drank for a couple of years after that, but I never again drank with any enjoyment. It was as if I'd seen myself for what I'd become and all that remained was to admit it.

The admitting took a while, and my family suffered mightily from my irrational moods and behavior during that time.

The news service assigned me to cover the national Democratic nominating convention in New York City in the summer of 1976. It was the nation's bicentennial. Tall sailing ships from all over the world filled New York Harbor, Jimmy Carter supporters filled the streets of Manhattan. It was a marvelous time to be alive and celebrating. I'd never been to New York City. Friends had given me lists of all the things to see and do. I spent every free moment in bars.

On the convention's final day, I went to lunch with another news service staffer at a cheap beer and burger joint just off Rockefeller Plaza. We drank until mid-afternoon. I returned to my hotel room to change, passed out on the bed and woke up at mid-evening, barely in time to rush to Madison Square Garden for a couple of half-baked interviews and back to the news service office to file one of the poorest stories I'd done in a long while.

That New York City trip seemed to unleash something inside me. Until then, while I'd been a frequent and heavy drinker, I'd managed some control, generally getting to assignments on time and writing fairly concise, professional stories. After my convention trip, I seemed unable to get the control I once had. Getting to work each day became a struggle. Focusing on what people were saying as I interviewed them became a nightmare. Writing a clear, complete news story without errors became all but impossible.

All these things happened gradually, but by the middle of 1977, I knew I had a drinking problem. I told my wife I would quit. If I can't handle it alone, I said, I promise I'll ask somebody for help. I didn't intend to ever do that. I wasn't about to let anyone besides my wife know I feared I was an alcoholic. I could stop drinking, but I couldn't be alcoholic.

I had the same misconceptions about "that kind of person" that most people did in those days. I knew alcoholics were weak-willed. I knew they had trouble with the law and couldn't hold a job and didn't support their families. I knew my bosses with the wire service wouldn't let me work for them if I couldn't drink because of an alcohol problem. In the first flush of my decision to go on the wagon, I told my supervisor I had some liver trouble. Just to be on the safe side, I was supposed to stay away from the booze, I said.

I couldn't do it, of course. Few people can get sober and stay that way without some kind of help. I wasn't among that few. Within weeks of my tearful confession to my wife, I began to drink again, in secret this time.

I hid bottles around the house, kept one in the garage, another in the bottom drawer at the office. I had to hide my drinking from everyone. Now it wasn't just a case of trying to control how much and how often I drank. I drank every day. I just had to drink in secret.

Each day became a lie. I struggled to seem sober. I gulped down breath mints and chewed gum constantly to mask the smell of liquor. I used eye drops to try to clear the redness that came back with each day's drinking. I withdrew from the family and from my friends. A person can't get trapped in an incoherent conversation if he doesn't talk to anyone.

The 1978 session of the South Dakota Legislature passed in a blur. I wrote story after story, filing them in a drunken haze and rushing frantically into the bureau the next morning to read what I'd written and see how many errors needed to be fixed.

I'd had my first drinking blackout in 1970, and it had become a source of great amusement at parties when I told of how I'd left the table at a bar downtown, headed for the restroom, and found myself in my garage after driving home and parking the car. I had a couple more of those incidents over the years. They were mildly alarming, but I could shrug them off with a shake of the head and a self-deprecating, "Boy, I must have tied one on last night."

By 1978, the blackouts were frequent, and frightening. Two, three, four afternoons a week I experienced periods ranging from a few minutes to several hours in which I functioned without knowing it. I'd be in the bureau typing, and suddenly I'd find myself finishing an interview with a legislator or taking notes during a news conference with the governor. I feared I was losing my mind, and I fought with myself to control the memory lapses.

Other reporters knew something was wrong. They didn't know what, so they did what they could. They covered for my lapses, made excuses when I couldn't be found late in the afternoons, cobbled together notes and wrote stories about meetings I'd missed.

After the 1978 session, I knew I needed more help than I could give myself. I called a recovering alcoholic in a city four hours away. He said he could help. Within an hour, two men I knew from Pierre walked into my office and said they would take me to a meeting of people who shared my problem.

I felt betrayed. The friend from out of town wasn't supposed to tell anyone in Pierre. Even so, these two men seemed so happy to help; I agreed to go to a meeting. I went back a couple of times a week for the next six months, but I kept on drinking. I wouldn't tell the others that. I

couldn't be honest. I used to leave meetings and cry about how the program was failing me. It wasn't, of course. I was failing myself by not being
honest. Even with my life falling apart all around me, I couldn't reveal my
secret openly to another person.

Blackouts came daily. I quit my news service job, took a salary cut
and went to work for a small newspaper in town. The news service didn't
understand me, I told people. They were out to get me. Well, they didn't
understand, that's true. I refused to let them know what was happening.
Instead, I took my secret and my bottle of cheap vodka, and I ran.

One afternoon as I slumped in a chair at home, my wife told me she
didn't want me around. I was no good to the children, no good to her and
no good to myself. She said I could keep living in the same house, but she
and the three children would plan their lives without me. They couldn't
count on me for anything, and they deserved some degree of normality in
their lives.

I could drink or not drink, she said. If I decided not to drink, she'd
do anything she could to help me. If I decided to continue drinking, she'd
do anything she had to to help herself.

When she walked out of the room, I was completely alone. Never in
my life had I felt so abandoned. I cried, told myself that all was lost. I sank
into a black pit of self-pity, convinced I'd die alone, drunk and unloved.
In my immature drunkenness, I wept for the lost promise of the child of
Marie and Henry Woster, the valedictorian of the class of 1962. I was lost
and pitiful.

The next day, although I'd gotten out of bed vowing not to drink,
I stopped at the municipal liquor store on the way to work. I bought a
quart of the cheapest vodka on the shelf and began to drink it by the coffee cupful as soon as I got to my office. Around noon I staggered to my
pickup to drive across the Missouri River Bridge for a photo assignment in
Fort Pierre.

That day was Oct. 12, 1978. In all the years since, I've been unable
to remember what happened and unable to find anyone who saw me and
who could help reconstruct my movements. I only know that I was cross-

ing the bridge one moment and sitting at the admissions desk at River Park the next.

Several hours had passed somehow. Glenn Jorgenson's sister, Nancy Tipton, worked at the center then. She told me later that she saw me stumbling down the hallway toward her desk and that I was begging for someone to help me. Apparently, during what had become my daily blackout, I'd driven to River Park, parked my pickup somewhere out in the park and asked to be checked in for alcohol treatment.

This was a Thursday. The paper I edited came out Friday, and I had done almost nothing to get stories written and set in type. If I stayed in River Park through the weekend, I'd avoid the problem of explaining why the paper hadn't been done and I'd have enough time to think up a story that would get me back into the office and back into the good graces of my family.

I agreed to stay in River Park that first night only because I had no other place to go and no one else who wanted me. It looked like a terrific place to hide out for a day or two.

I fell into bed that night exhausted, still half-drunk but fully intending to get up the following morning and make up a wonderful story that would let me walk out the front door.

When I woke up that first morning in the treatment center, I didn't have an urge to take a drink. Until that morning, every day for the past two or three years had brought an overpowering need to have a drink. Some mornings I'd be hung over, and some mornings I'd be sick, vomiting up dried blood from a stomach being eaten raw by alcohol. But always I'd burn with the desire for a drink.

That morning in River Park I was thirsty, my head hurt, my body ached and my stomach churned around. I didn't know if I could stand up, I couldn't keep my hands from shaking, and I wondered what would become of me in all the relationships I'd destroyed over the years. But I didn't want to drink alcohol. The obsession or compulsion or craving that had controlled my waking life for so long had disappeared.

That's why I say God must have done it. I never intended to go to treatment, but in a blackout I got there. I never intended to stay, but my need for alcohol left me even as I prepared to plot a way out of this mess. I didn't do that. It simply happened to me.

Waking up and not needing a drink, I felt the first, faint stirring of hope I'd had in such a long while. Maybe, I thought, if I stay here a while, listen to what's going on and try to absorb the program, maybe I can stop drinking. It's worked for other people. Perhaps it can work for me.

It did. I never drank again, and my 30 days in River Park started me on a path of sobriety that has been more rewarding than I could have imagined. I found a group of people just like me, alcoholics trying to learn to live without booze, pills or street drugs.

I learned that an alcoholic is an alcoholic. The retired mail carrier that drank whiskey had many of the same issues as the 17-year-old ranch girl who smoked marijuana and drank beer or the 30-year-old construction worker who swilled tap beer and injected heroin. Each of them had to learn to face life without chemicals. So did I.

Few encounters were easy. I felt a tremendous anxiety the first time I met Jorgenson after I'd stumbled into River Park. After all, I hadn't written the stories on his television series. I'd ignored a couple of other invitations to visit and here I was an alcoholic, just like the people he worked around every day. I thought he might have a snide remark or two when he saw me, but he simply smiled, shook my hand and said, "I'm glad you got here. It's a good place to be."

It was a good place to be. It saved my life.

Some years after I went through treatment, River Park closed its Pierre center. A lot of alcoholics who first found hope there mourned the passing of the unassuming treatment center by the river. I wrote a column for the Pierre newspaper, (the *Daily Capital Journal* at that time), and I tried to capture some of what River Park in Pierre meant to those of us who found sobriety there. Here's what I wrote:

> It's empty now, quiet and gray-shadowed as a crypt in a hor-
> ror movie. But nothing is frightening here, nothing threatening.
> It's only empty.
> An irregular square of light squeezes through the glass at the
> end of the narrow hall and drops noiselessly to the thick carpet.

Bedrooms line each side of the concrete-block hallway like ca-
dets ready for inspection, but a few doors gape open like missing
teeth in an old hobo's grin.

The emptiness is so real that you try not to exhale, conscious
of each breath scraping like a rasp across a piece of oak. The still-
ness hugs the hallway like thick fog on the main street of a ghost
town, or the remembered devotion in the back pew of a church
on a moonless night.

This is a wing of the old convent between St. Mary's Hospital
and Maryhouse nursing home. For 14 years, until last Saturday, it
was River Park, temporary home and lasting hope for thousands
of misery-laden people hooked on alcohol or other drugs.

Now, it's only empty.

Now, if you stand in the murky shadows long enough, it is
like a ghost town or an empty church. Gradually, you begin to
hear whispering echoes of 14 years worth of spirits.

Faintly at first, but distinctly, the sounds of the place spread
through the hall, scattering the shadows.

There's laughter here, full and free. It's a bright and clean
sound, because these people needed each other and learned
quickly to laugh at themselves and with their fellow clients.

There are voices, soft or loud, hesitant and stammering,
direct and certain.

Many come from the lecture room, where those who had
already taken the first steps in the process of recovery from a
common illness shared their experience, strength and hope
with those just beginning the journey. Other voices, too, can be
traced to small groups of clients, two here, three there, quietly
sharing failings and fears and starting to realize that, with each
other's help, they just might make it.

There's the sound of pages being turned in a search for
answers, and the scurrying sound of pens filling notebook pages
with the suffering of the past and the promise of better times.

There is crying. The controlled moan of a girl who, although barely 17, despairs of ever feeling good again. The heart-stopping sobs of a man who has hurt the ones he loves the most too many times to count. The chest-shaking, soundless cry of one who has finally forgiven herself, of another who at last understands that he isn't alone.

And always, there is the chorus of thousands of voices saying, "Yes, I felt just that way, too. Yes, I understand exactly what you feel."

River Park has moved inpatient treatment to Rapid City and Sioux Falls. It has outreach centers scattered in many other cities.

But for thousands, River Park will forever be what they hear in the faint echoes in these narrow, gray-shadowed hallways.

This book was written after I'd had many in-depth conversations with Glenn Jorgenson to capture his thoughts and reflections on the inspiration for River Park. I also reviewed nearly the entire collection of interviews Glenn did for the *It's Great To Be Alive* television series.

River Park helped me at a time when I believed nothing and no one could. Jorgenson and his staff of counselors and nurses made me realize I was capable of a normal, alcohol-free life. I left treatment knowing that I owed the place and the people more than I could ever repay. I tried in small ways, going to the center once a month to tell my story to the new clients, stopping by from time to time to try to help still-shaky drunks believe that their stay would be worthwhile, even returning each Saturday evening for years to join the guitar players for the sing-along.

None of those things balanced the books. Perhaps helping to tell the story of this amazing place and the people who made it so will put one more payment back for all I took from it. I'd like to think so.

—Terry Woster

Chapter One

Glenn's Journey

Glenn Jorgenson stood at the edge of the road at the crest of Minnesota hill and looked across the town of Sioux Falls. He raised his right thumb to indicate he was hoping to catch a ride out of town—and as far as a motorist would take him toward the West Coast. His left hand clutched a suitcase bursting with dreams.

The hilltop offered a view of a community bustling with post-war activity. Jorgenson couldn't see that, though. He'd had his fill of Sioux Falls, South Dakota.

His future, he believed, lay far to the west, out in California. He'd heard amazing stories of Los Angeles, San Jose, and San Francisco. They were the names of cities that made up the heart of the garden spot of the United States. California was a magical place, a place the Great Depression had missed, a place that wasn't bothered with the sacrifices being asked of a war-weary nation in the wake of the surrenders of Japan and Germany. A fellow could go out to California and be a big shot in no time. And boy, wouldn't that be a change from dreary little South Dakota?

Oh, sure, Glenn reflected as he stood by the road waiting for a ride, he'd had some good times in South Dakota, especially in Sioux Falls during a summer of work for a doctor. He'd seen some amazing people, too - the wealthy people who golfed and played tennis and feasted and partied, who spent money on clothes and cars and food and liquor as if they'd never heard of the Great Depression

How did they manage that? Back home in sleepy Hayti, South Dakota, everyone had been touched by the dust storms and grasshoppers, the failed crops and failed banks.

And before the farmers and shop owners of Hamlin County could even start to catch up as the depression lifted, the war came. Hayti folks were as patriotic as anyone, and when President Roosevelt asked the country to sacrifice, Jorgenson's hometown responded. They grew victory gardens, spent what little money they had for war bonds, and carefully rationed gasoline and meat and tires. They did without, all of them, and for a youngster growing up with a head full of big dreams, a little farming town that's doing without looks pretty dreary.

Glenn's father, Lloyd Jorgenson, held one of the important positions in Hayti—county auditor. That meant an impressive office in the stately old county courthouse. It meant—as long as the voters didn't turn on him—a steady, if meager, salary and a check to stretch from one payday to the next. It also meant connections with political people in other parts of the state.

When Glenn was 13, those connections paid off. Glenn landed a job as a yard boy for a Sioux Falls doctor. The doctor had a cabin near Hayti, where he and some of his friends came hunting. Glenn ran errands for them, then watched as the hunters prepared their meals and cleaned their game. As they cleaned and cooked, the men talked about hunting and business deals and money. They'd pause now and then to take man-sized gulps of whiskey from tall cocktail glasses, and they'd wipe their mouths and smack their lips appreciatively as the liquor went down their throats.

When the doctor offered to take Glenn in for the next summer, the Jorgensen's could hardly say no. Money was scarce in Hayti and on the surrounding farms. If Glenn could make a few dollars in Sioux Falls and get room and board besides, it would lift a tremendous load from his parents' shoulders.

Glenn didn't like the idea of spending the summer away from his friends and family. In fact, the thought of being that far away for that long had him just plain scared. Not that he'd let anyone know that. Especially his father. Norwegian blood coursed through the Jorgenson family's veins, and the Norwegians had settled much of the harsh and unforgiving prairie of Hamlin County. They didn't complain. They did their duty.

So Glenn entered a new world that summer of his 13th year. It was a world of affluence and influence, populated by men and women who knew that living well required money and enjoying the good life required liquor. When the boy from the small town landed a job caddying at the Minnehaha Country Club, he got a glimpse of the power and moneyed elite of South Dakota. He liked what he saw, and he promised himself that someday, he'd live like that.

The Norwegian work ethic never deserted him, though. Besides mowing and raking and running errands for the doctor, and carrying heavy golf bags for the country-club set, Glenn landed a job downtown in Sioux Falls at a theater owned by Joe Floyd. Floyd also created and developed the Midcontinent Broadcasting Company. His company's flagship property, KELO-TV, grew into perhaps the most powerful instrument of mass communication in the state.

Glenn Jorgenson couldn't know it at the time, but his association with Floyd and KELO-TV would be a key to the life he'd live much, much later. For now, the biggest thing in Glenn's life was finding a way to have the good things. He'd never seen the kinds of social outings that were so common in Sioux Falls. Society did a lot of partying. And partying meant social drinking, a phrase that struck Glenn as just the right sort of activity for people who were just a little bit better than the average shop keeper back in Hayti.

Glenn knew all about drinking. He'd learned at an early age that people who drank too much were weak and worthy only of pity. He'd heard the phrase "town drunk," pronounced with a disgusted tone. He'd seen a few of the local men stumble as they left the main street tavern, and he'd heard talk between his parents about this person or that who drank to excess. It was a sinful thing to do.

Glenn surely had felt shame and guilt that time his 12-year-old pal had swiped some liquor from his parents and the two of them experimented with alcohol. Glenn wound up passing out on the courthouse lawn. When he awoke, he felt not only shame for his weakness and guilt for his sinfulness but fear at the thought that someone could have come along and found him. That's what comes of drinking, the 12-year-old Glenn told himself. And yet, why did he feel so good after that first sip or two?

And what about the hunters at the doctor's cabin by the lake? They all drank sometimes. The brown liquid was as much a part of the hunt as the Purdy shotguns and orange game pouches. Yet these were decent, hardworking and highly successful men. They certainly didn't appear ashamed of taking a cocktail now and then. Why should it be all right for them and not for Glenn, who planned to mix with their like someday?

And, what of the social set in Sioux Falls? Drinking made the parties. Glenn had seen that for himself. These bright, influential and successful men and women raised champagne glasses and sipped martinis. As the night grew longer, the talk grew louder, the laughter easier and the friendships more intense. How could that be wrong?

Ah, but that was social drinking. And among people of good taste and refinement, social drinking happened a lot. If the folks back home in Hayti didn't understand that, well, Glenn Jorgenson didn't plan to spend his whole life in that little farm town, not by a long shot.

He'd seen enough to know that his place was a lot higher than a county seat in small-town South Dakota. That might be enough for his father, but Glenn wanted more than that. He wasn't about to scrape for a few dollars a week in a dusty old town. He had more ambition than that. And more talent, too. He had dreams and he was going places—big places.

Many of the folks of Hayti expected the same great things from young Glenn that he himself did. Wasn't he always in the library reading one book after another? And wasn't he one of the best athletes Hamlin County had turned out in a long while? In a town where high school basketball was king, Glenn had developed his skills well enough to play on the varsity team for the Hayti Redbirds as early as eighth grade. Not many kids did that, did they?

Glenn knew he was a pretty darned good basketball player. He suspected, too, that he was probably a lot smarter than the average person in Hayti. Sometimes, though, he wished other people wouldn't think so. Sometimes he wasn't sure if he was as talented as those people said or as intelligent, either. They expected so much from him. It was one thing to have big dreams for yourself, but what if you weren't good enough to meet the town's expectations?

Glenn sometimes wondered if there was something wrong inside him when he thought that way. *I know I'm way better than the average person in Hayti, so why do I have these doubts? It isn't fair for people to expect so much from me. It's none of their business. But, boy, would they all be proud of me if I really became famous or rich. But what if I can't do it? What if I'm just a phony? How could I ever face these people again?*

Quite by accident, Glenn found an answer to that question. Liquor. Not so long after his humiliating experience of passing out on the court-house lawn, Glenn had a chance to drink again. He took more care this time, recognizing alcohol as a powerful force and treating it with the respect any powerful force deserves. In return, it seemed, alcohol treated Glenn with respect. It rewarded his cautious approach. After just one or two drinks, his doubts were gone. Another drink or two, and all the big dreams came back, more clearly than he'd ever seen them before.

Oh, my goodness, yes. I am meant to do great things, he thought. *I won't let these people down. I'm respected, and well liked. The girls in school think I'm pretty good looking, and they're right. The adults see how special I am, too. My name is in the sport pages all the time. It's just false modesty to sit around worrying about whether I'll be successful. Of course I will be. I'll go out in the world and become an important man. I know I will.*

If it took a few drinks of liquor every now and then to keep the old spirit up, why, what was wrong with that? The other kids were drinking some, too. In fact, it was like being part of a club or something. It was a lot like being in the country club in Sioux Falls. Of course a person had to watch how much he drank, sure. But, after that time he'd drunk so much he'd passed out in public, who'd be stupid enough to let himself get out of control with liquor like that again? Glenn knew he was smart, and smart people could control their liquor.

That didn't mean not drinking. In fact, one of the things Glenn had learned by hanging around the social set was that drinking a lot but not letting it affect you was an accomplishment people admired greatly.

"Boy, that guy really knows how to hold his liquor," was the highest praise the smart set could bestow. Glenn had heard people say that time and again. The experience taught Glenn two important lessons, lessons he'd cling to for much of his early adult life.

First, having the ability to be a social drinker was a major asset, as long as you were always able to keep your senses, meet your commitments and do the job expected of you. The only real shame in drinking was to be so weak that you couldn't get to work the next day and give your boss a full day's labor.

Second, not drinking wasn't the good thing he'd sometimes been led to believe as a young boy. People in the social and business world looked at the teetotaler as a little odd.

The answer was to learn to drink when the occasion demanded and to keep a tight rein on how much you drank—to be known as one of those guys "who can really hold his liquor." Glenn saw quickly that he must become that kind of man. And he knew he could do it, too. He could do anything he set his mind to doing.

Becoming successful was one thing he'd set his mind to. About the only thing as important as success in Glenn's life during his school days was winning the affections of a dark-haired slip of a farm girl named Phyllis. She was younger, just a freshman when Glenn was in his final year of high school. But she had a streak of common sense far beyond her years, and she was just about the nicest person he'd ever met. And she sure was pretty.

Phyllis wasn't the first woman who'd caught Glenn's attention. By the time he was a senior, he'd become something of a good-time Charlie—going with classmates to dance halls and saloons in nearby towns. Sometimes the guys would run into bar girls. They were usually older women, and a guy could take one look at them and just know they'd experienced a whole lot more than any high school boy had ever imagined. Still, they were fun to joke around with, have a few drinks with, and nobody was thinking of taking one of them home to meet the folks and start making wedding plans.

Once in a while—in spite of his best intentions—Glenn went on one of these party nights and drank way too much. It didn't happen every time, but it happened more than Glenn would have liked it to. Once, he passed out in the back seat of a car. It was only 26 degrees, and when he awoke, he told himself in alarm, I could have frozen to death.

That incident reminded him of his earlier resolve to be one of those guys who can really hold his liquor. He made a new resolution to be even more careful next time. And he was, too. The next time, the time after that, and maybe a third time still. Sooner or later, though, he did it again—drinking himself into a stupor and waking up wondering where he was, how he got there, how he'd get himself out of this one without humiliating himself or his family.

That period of Glenn's life was a good time for learning excuses. If a person couldn't always keep his promise to drink in a controlled, social way, there must be a reason. One night it was because he drank some of his friends' vodka after polishing off his own pint of whiskey. Everyone knows you don't mix your liquors. Another time it was because the liquor was so cheap. Everyone knows you can have strange reactions to those off-brands of booze. The good-quality alcohol, measured by the price on the tag that hangs around the neck of the bottle, isn't so damaging to a person's system. It doesn't leave you with a hangover, either, he told himself, the way some of these cheap whiskeys can.

Late in his high school days, Glenn began to experience excruciating headaches. They were almost blinding in their severity, and they frightened him terribly. He came to realize that he could sense when one of the attacks was coming on, but he was helpless to stop them and almost unable to withstand the fierce pain. Some days, when one of the more violent of the attacks was upon him, it was all he could do to lie on his bed in a darkened room, pressing a cool cloth to his forehead and pleading with God to make the pain go away. When the spell passed, he was left weak and shaken. He began to search for ways to dull the pain.

The headaches and the drinking binges were both things Glenn sometimes feared he couldn't control as he neared the end of his high school years. His Norwegian parents brought him up to understand that life isn't always easy. Complaining only wasted time and energy, and there was always someone else worse off than you were. Glenn knew that while his parents would sympathize with his suffering, there wasn't anything they could do for him.

And he dared not speak about his occasional binges of out-of-control drinking, although he worried sometimes that he hadn't matured enough to control that sort of thing as well as he knew he'd need to do when he became a successful lawyer or businessman or politician. Had he ever decided to talk to his parents about drinking, neither of them would have understood how he could allow himself to get in such condition. So he kept it all inside, fighting off the pain and coping with the fear by thoughts of Phyllis and the life together they'd have—once he'd gotten college out of the way in California and she'd finished high school.

✳ ✳ ✳

As he tossed his suitcase into the trunk of the first car that stopped, Glenn took one last look from the top of Minnesota hill. Nope, not much here he'd miss. Only Phyllis, and he'd be back soon enough to take her west and begin a real life, just as soon as he'd made a success of himself.

So much for big dreams.

California turned out to be a place of loneliness, of disillusionment, of often solitary drinking, blinding headaches and paralyzing self-doubts. Glenn struggled in college, nagged by a feeling that his South Dakota schooling had ill-prepared him for California's system of higher education. The loneliness dogged him. He drank with some kids at school from time to time, but he never really felt like he had any friends. When he lost a job that had helped pay his college costs, he knew it was time to go home. At least in Hayti he had family who cared about him and knew how smart he was. And he had Phyllis, who treated him as if he were a white knight.

It seemed he'd been in California an eternity, but when the bus pulled into the Sioux Falls station, it had only been a matter of months. Coming home like this embarrassed him—no job, no money, and no big success. He'd had to borrow the money for the bus ticket back to South Dakota.

His old pool-hall buddies welcomed him home, though. And Phyllis, she'd never be critical of a decision Glenn made. He was the man she intended to marry, after all.

Glenn quickly found a job at a grocery store. The work didn't challenge his intellect or showcase his special talents, but it was a beginning. He tried to enlist in the Navy, getting as far as Fargo, North Dakota, before a military doctor rejected him because of curvature of the spine. That shook his self-esteem. But he told himself it was the Navy's loss.

His uncle Shorty loaned him $300—enough for nine months at General Beadle State Teacher's College, and with that certification he taught fourth through eighth grades at a tiny school in Dempster, South Dakota. He liked teaching but the salary wouldn't support a family, and he was thinking seriously about marriage. When in 1951 Governor Sigurd Anderson offered him the opportunity to be assistant director of the new state department of old age and survivors insurance, his thoughts turned to action. He married his high-school sweetheart and moved to South Dakota's capital city to begin a life of happily ever after.

An important man with a wife and a state administrator's job, Glenn found in Pierre the life he'd fantasized about since he was a young boy. He moved smoothly from the hard work of the day to the relaxing companionship of the happy hour, and he spent long, heady hours talking politics and planning Young Republican strategy with like-minded capitol-city business and government leaders.

A rising star in the GOP, he left Phyllis for a weekend in Brookings, where General Dwight Eisenhower was speaking at a party function. He returned home tired, hung over from far too many drinks, but buoyed by the face-to-face meeting with Ike and bursting to tell Phyllis the story of her husband and the important things he'd been doing.

He walked into an empty house.

What is this? he fumed, suddenly hurt as if Phyllis had somehow conspired to put a damper on one of the biggest moments in his life. She can't even bother to be home when I need her? What about supper? I've had a long weekend, and I wanted to share all the excitement with her. Still in a foul temper when his sister walked in, Glenn yelled, "Where the hell is Phyllis?"

She was in the hospital, his sister told him. She had a miscarriage. The news stunned Glenn. He didn't know she was pregnant. Why wouldn't she tell him they were going to have a baby? Why didn't she call when she miscarried?

Phyllis didn't want him to be bothered, Glenn's sister told him. It was such an important weekend for him. Oh, did that unleash an attack of guilt. Glenn rushed to the hospital, wrapped his arms around his small wife, and promised over and over he'd never be gone again when she needed him. Children will come in time, he told her. Meanwhile, they'd just live for each other, he said. Happily ever after.

Living happily ever after wasn't easy, though, not when the job was boring, not when the boss took all the credit for Glenn's good ideas and relentless effort. He put up with it as long as he could, but finally Glenn went to Phyllis and suggested they move to California. Maybe it didn't work out for him when he tried it there on his own. They'd be there together this time, he told her. That would make all the difference, for both of them.

The job market boomed on the West Coast, he said, and the pay scale couldn't be matched anywhere in the Midwest. They'd never forgive themselves if they didn't gamble a little this time.

Phyllis told Glenn she was content with her clerical job in a state agency. After he painted more mental pictures of streets of gold and trees laden with greenbacks, she agreed that California might be the best place to be—if it made Glenn happy.

California turned out to be almost an instant replay of Glenn's earlier visit, except that this time, while he had no luck finding a good job, Phyllis began working almost immediately. And just as quickly she seemed to settle into a life of working during the day and keeping a home going in the evenings and on weekends. For his part, Glenn gambled a little, bought drinks for prosperous-looking gentlemen in classy lounges and tried to stifle the mounting despair over his inability, once again, to be a success in California. The headaches came with increasing frequency and intensity, and he began to take shots of Demerol to control the pain.

Finally, he told Phyllis they should return to South Dakota. It hurt him deeply, he told her, to see her so unhappy and so far from her family. She readily agreed to pack up and return to the Midwest if that's what Glenn needed to make him happy. He assured her it was only her happiness that concerned him, and he knew South Dakota was the place she'd be happiest.

Fortune smiled on the Jorgensons when they returned to Pierre. Phyllis quickly found a job in a state agency. Glenn found a backer willing to loan him the money to buy a credit business. For a while after he returned from California, Glenn even managed to control his drinking, with occasional lapses to celebrate a special event or toast a friend's success. He worked hard, and the business prospered.

At home, things were prosperous, too. Glenn and Phyllis found a home in a quiet neighborhood of tall elm and hackberry trees. With the house came extra bedrooms, and the opportunity to fill one with a child. Phyllis became pregnant, and in due time Glenn found himself staring in awe at the most beautiful baby girl in the world.

The blessed event called for a celebration. While Phyllis recovered from childbirth in the hospital, Glenn went on the town with his best friend. He awoke from a wild, giddy night of drinking with a giant hangover and the resolve to straighten up again. Fatherhood brought new responsibility, and he promised himself he'd never do anything to hurt his newborn daughter.

He applied himself to his work, but in his free time, Glenn immersed himself in politics. He gravitated naturally to the strategy sessions, the happy-hour meetings that began after work and stretched, more and more often it seemed, through the supper hour. He and the gang he ran with backed a candidate for governor—a solid Republican, a sure bet in conservative South Dakota. Only two Democrats had been elected governor in state history, and one of them rode in on the Franklin Delano Roosevelt tide during the Depression years.

Although Phyllis became pregnant again, Glenn had to travel the campaign trail, a long, demanding grind that he told her would cement their successful future together when the candidate took office and divided the spoils of political victory. The campaign ended on election night with a gala victory celebration planned in the banquet room of a Pierre hotel.

The celebration became a wake for Glenn as the unthinkable happened—the Democrat won. Glenn hardly noticed. Sometime during the evening, as every new set of voter returns darkened the gloom of the candidate's staff and volunteers, Glenn had grabbed a bottle and adjourned to a private room in the hotel, drowning the bitterness of defeat with shot after shot of burning liquor.

He awoke sick, hung over and unable to recall whether his candidate had won the election. He returned home to find that he'd become a father again. While he'd been mourning the defeat of a candidate, Phyllis had been laboring to bring the couple's second daughter into the world.

Again, he promised himself he'd be better at home, better at work, better in every way. Again, the resolve lasted a while. Then again he began to drink more, stay out more, travel more. Phyllis became less understanding of his absences, his drinking, his need to always be scheming and dreaming. She began scheduling activities for herself and the girls, activities they could count on with or without Glenn. His headaches came back, stronger and more frequent than ever. The headaches seemed to be worse when he drank, Phyllis told him. Perhaps he shouldn't drink?

Instead, Glenn began to worry that the headaches were a sign of some mental illness. He consulted counselors, psychiatrists, and doctors. Nothing helped, so he drank again, took more pills, begged for Demerol when the headaches became blinding. And through it all, he kept charging ahead, looking for business opportunities, buying a second credit bureau, investing in land, joining a friend to open a private club. Some of the business ventures succeeded, others failed miserably. But success or failure, they showed that Glenn Jorgenson was a man to be reckoned with, a visionary and a builder, the kind of person whose counsel would be valued by any leader.

And, eventually, a leader did want Glenn's advice and counsel. Six years had passed since the losing campaign of the sure-thing Republican. The upstart Democrat lost a re-election bid, and the GOP regained control of the governor's office. The new chief executive, Nils Boe, asked Glenn to join him as director of state personnel. A cabinet position, Glenn thought with smug satisfaction as he dialed his buddy to suggest a celebration of drinks.

This time, what seemed to be an unlimited opportunity turned out to be a sickening, downward spiral. While he succeeded in developing personnel policies and spearheaded efforts to establish a retirement program for public employees, his personal life suffered. Important government managers need more than ever to be able to relax with a few drinks after work, to meet other important folks for drinks in the evening, to bring important people home to dinner on a whim and without warning Phyllis. Glenn threw himself into that routine with almost a vicious energy, working long days and drinking late into the nights.

Sometimes, usually when he was the most hung over and washed out, Glenn looked at his life and saw nothing but an abyss. His world seemed to have so little meaning. His family—for they had two daughters by now, daughters who loved their daddy and who could break his heart with a smile or a tear—was everything to him, yet he stayed out late, missed school events and ballet recitals and even church programs. He came home drunk, slurring his words and smelling of whiskey and cigarettes. The hurt expression on Phyllis's face cut him so deeply that he prayed for her to be angry when he'd come in late, full of lies and wild excuses. Her anger he could counter with anger of his own. Her sadness and pain, those he couldn't bear.

In those times, Glenn couldn't completely hide the gnawing voice inside that whispered: "You aren't normal. Are you crazy? Is it the liquor? Maybe you have a drinking problem."

When he couldn't silence the voice, he'd groan inwardly and hug himself as if to keep his soul from flying out of his body. This can't go on, he'd moan.

"I am not this kind of person, I'm a good man," he'd cry to the heavens, as if the God of his childhood would hear him, reach down and make everything all right again.

In his despair, he turned even more frequently to drink, and to pills, for his headaches were becoming more frequent and more completely unbearable. He refused to look on the pills as drugs. These were prescription medicines, given him by licensed and trained pharmacists, never mind that as he took and required more and more of the pills, he began to see more and more doctors in different towns as he traveled.

Liquor, of course, he could get. Nothing easier. Every tavern and lounge and supper club and after-hours spot in the state sold booze. Glenn came to know bartenders and waitresses in establishments from Sioux Falls to Rapid City, and they came to know him. The bars and country club lounges outside of Pierre became sanctuaries, in fact, away from the prying eyes and wagging tongues of the hometown folks. In the big city, a well-spoken man with an expensive suit and a wallet full of cash merited respect. Glenn sought out excuses to travel.

But he couldn't continue drinking forever, though he often wished he could. He recalled a scene from an old Ed Sullivan variety show on television, the act in which a man tries to keep dozens of dinner plates spinning on slender poles. Glenn often felt like that man, rushing from pole to pole, frantically trying to add just a little more motion to the plate without sending it crashing to the ground. No one could keep so many plates in the air for so long. It was just too hard.

His work slipped, and he drank. Phyllis cried softly, and he drank. The girls looked at him sadly when he returned home from the bar too late to go to the school play. And he drank.

The job disappeared. He found another. He lost that one, and his closest friend gave him a chance to manage a bar and motel. The very first night, he closed up the bar with a group of old drinking buddies. Within days, he found himself peering with bloodshot eyed into the tortured face of his best friend in all the world and struggling to comprehend the words he was hearing:

"Sorry, Glenn, but it just isn't going to work out. We have to let you go."

Glenn snatched a bottle of whiskey from the shelf behind the bar and fled unsteadily to a vacant room in the motel. He drank himself into oblivion, regaining consciousness long enough to see Phyllis standing beside his rumpled bed.

"Glenn, I love you," she said. 'I would do anything to help you but there is nothing I can do. Either get help or the girls and I are gone."

The motel room door closed sotftly behind her. Glenn groped for his bottle. It was empty. He'd never been so alone. Betrayed by his closest friend, forgotten by his employer, unloved and unwanted by his family, forsaken by God.

"There's nothing left," he cried. "I'm finished."

And thus began his recovery.

Chapter Two

Hitting Bottom

More than 15 million people in the United States are alcoholics. Experts have argued for decades about the cause. Were they born that way? Are they a product of their environment? Did some cataclysmic mental, emotional or genetic change occur that turned them forever from someone who could handle alcohol in a socially acceptable way into an out-of-control drinker or addict?

Whatever the first cause, the plain fact remains that millions of people in this country are on the same path Glenn Jorgenson's life took. If they haven't already reached that pit of despair that made Jorgenson cry out, "I'm finished," then they're on the way. And it's a painful, lonely journey.

Ask Johnny Cash.

As he tells it in the River Park television series *It's Great to be Alive*, the country singing legend came literally within minutes of losing his life to alcohol. Lost in a dark cave in rural Georgia as he tried to run from the demons of alcohol and pills, Cash discovered that the difference between life and almost certain death was as small as a faint breath of moving air. The slight breeze through the utter blindness of a pitch-black cave helped Cash find the way to the entrance and help.

But that only came after he'd given up, after he'd turned the whole business of living or dying over to a Higher Power, crying out, "Dear God, I can't handle it."

What turns a successful, famous entertainer like Johnny Cash into a wretched soul lost in the dark emptiness of a cave with nothing left to cling to but a desperate prayer?

Drugs. Mind- and mood-altering chemicals.

For Cash the combination was alcohol, barbiturates, and amphetamines.

"People take drugs because they make you feel good," he said. "I took the pills so long, and then the pills started taking from me."

Like most chemically dependent men and women, though, Cash refused for a long time to look at what his alcohol and drug use was doing to his life, his career and his relationships with other people.

"There's a demon called deception," he said. "I was drinking a case of beer a day and taking uppers and downers."

When his wife came to find him during an extended binge of drinking, Cash fled to cave country in a remote part of Georgia. He'd always been something of a spelunker, a person who finds excitement and adventure exploring the depths of caves, but this time he was out of control. Emotionally disoriented, physically fatigued and spiritually drained, he wandered aimlessly through the dark tunnels. The charge in his flashlight batteries grew weaker and weaker as he stumbled over the rock floor of the cave. Finally, the dim yellow beam of light simply disappeared, and the thick midnight blackness swallowed Cash.

That's when he gave up and prayed.

"It was so dark you could feel it," Cash recalled. "I lay down flat on my back and said, 'Dear God, I can't handle it.'"

Sounds almost exactly like the words Glenn Jorgenson spoke alone in that motel room in the gripping scene from his moment of truth, doesn't it?

So, two men, one a world-famous country music singer, the other a once successful government administrator and private business operator. Both intelligent, engaging, and effective in their dealings with other people. Both used their talents and drive to climb to the top of their chosen professions.

Yet both have found themselves alone and in utter despair. Both started out using alcohol as a way to release tension and express feelings. They found pleasure in a glass of wine or bottle of beer. It made them feel good, as Cash put it.

In that, they were no different from millions and millions of other, ordinary people all over the world who use alcohol in one or another of the many ways that fall under the general heading of alcoholism.

It is a disease, not a weakness or a personal failing.

That wasn't what people believed when Glenn Jorgenson was a boy growing up in the farming community of Hayti. Back then, people believed the alcoholic was weak-willed, mentally ill, even just plain sinful and unwilling to change.

"There was such a stigma when I was growing up, and it was still incredibly strong when we began to work in the field of alcohol treatment," Jorgenson said. "People would be looked down on for admitting they were alcoholic. It was the kind of admission that could result in being fired, and it all but routinely caused the person to be ostracized by the rest of the community."

Jorgenson had lived with the fear of being exposed as a problem drinker all of his adult life. Even as a young boy just experimenting with a stolen cupful of whiskey or a bottle of beer at a summer picnic, he understood how powerful was the public stigma attached to the weak, pitiful souls who couldn't handle their liquor and who seemed to need it too much.

And if Jorgenson understood that stigma and feared its power, how much more must Betty Ford have understood and feared it?

She grew up before women's liberation—coming of age at a time when a double standard ruled and the two sexes were often judged differently for the same actions.

"To be an addict and a woman is to be doubly stigmatized," Ford says in an *It's Great to be Alive* segment. "Somehow, it's okay for a man to be a drinker. A woman who is a drunk is a tramp. People have to realize that alcoholism is a disease."

Betty Ford certainly didn't set out to become an alcoholic. In fact, as she says, she learned at an early age that it was incredibly important to "always be a lady."

She carried that knowledge into her marriage with Gerald Ford, a marriage that thrust her into the public spotlight as the wife of a high-level government official.

The spotlight shone more and more brightly on the Fords as Gerald moved up the political ladder. He worked hard and advanced from a young congressman representing a single district in Michigan to top Republican leader in the U.S. House of Representatives. As the Watergate scandal of the early 1970s toppled one powerful figure after another, Ford moved to the very center of power in Washington, D.C. Appointed vice president by President Richard Nixon after Spiro Agnew's resignation, Ford became the nation's president in August of 1974 when Nixon himself resigned office.

Betty Ford was alone a lot in the days when her husband was a congressman. She drank sometimes to soothe the loneliness. She drank sometimes to ease the resentment about being the one left at home.

"It was a very controlled drinking,'" Betty Ford said. "But I realize I did use it to deal with some resentments."

Gerald Ford's heady rise to power and influence swept Betty along, too, and soon she didn't have much time for drinking. Prescription drugs weren't the same as drinking, though, and they did substitute duty to ease the nerves, the resentments and the pressures.

With Gerald Ford's election defeat in 1976, though, the time in the spotlight ended. It was back to being a private citizen, to being former President Ford. And Betty Ford became the former first lady.

"I felt a great depression," she remembers. "I had no responsibilities."

She also had no real reason not to drink, and she began to use alcohol more heavily than before. In combination with the medication she continued to take, the effect was electric and immediate.

Betty Ford knows from experience what those who study alcoholism and alcoholics have discovered from observation. It's a progressive disease. That means that, once a person begins to drink in an alcoholic fashion, the disease will grow progressively worse, even if the person quits using alcohol for some period of time.

If an alcoholic is dry for a period of five years, for example, the disease progresses. Should that person begin to drink again, the disease will pick up, as if there'd never been an interruption. The person will discover that when he or she begins to drink again, the drinking pattern won't be the same as it was when the drinking was interrupted. Instead, the drinking will be that of a person who had continued to drink all those five years.

That happened to Betty Ford.

When she began drinking in an unrestricted way after her husband's defeat, she discovered the progressive nature of alcoholism. "That's when it hit hard," she said.

Like Johnny Cash, like Glenn Jorgenson, Betty Ford refused to admit she had a problem.

"Denial is probably one of the strongest symptoms of this disease," she said.

In her refusal to see how liquor and pills were destroying her life, Betty Ford had, for the longest time, willing if unwitting accomplices in her family, who also refused to see the changes slowly taking place in her life.

"While I had my denial, my family had their denial, too," Betty Ford said. She was a wife, a mother, a grandmother, and a recognized national figure, one of America's most admired people.

"For me to be an alcoholic was not acceptable," she said. "Their denial allowed my alcoholism to progress."

Looking back at her life then, Betty Ford can see the signs that she was powerless over alcohol. She'd have conversations with her daughter, and then later be unable to remember what was said. Sometimes, frighteningly, she couldn't remember even having had the earlier conversation at all.

But it was from those kinds of incidents that she found her way to recovery. Her daughter, Susan, went to other members of the Ford family and told them of her fears that her mother was drinking too much. It took a while, but the family arranged for what is called an intervention.

Family members, carefully coached by a specialist in the field of alcohol treatment, gathered with Betty Ford. Calmly and simply they took turns telling of times when her drinking had caused them pain or worry. They told her they loved her, and they wanted her to find help. Susan even told her she was reluctant to leave the grandchildren with Betty, fearful for their safety if their grandmother should drink too much.

For Betty Ford, that was the moment of surrender.

Alcoholics call it hitting bottom. That's a term used to refer to the moment when an addict has completely given up. It can come in a cave, or a motel room, a living room or a death-row cell. Sometimes the bottom can be a street gutter, where a wretched man or woman lies with no home, no family, no job and no hope. Other times, the bottom isn't physically that low, although emotionally, mentally and spiritually it's impossible to measure just how bottomless despair can feel.

With growing public awareness that alcoholism is a disease, with more treatment centers and more active chapters of Alcoholics Anonymous, the bottom has been raised. That's what the men and women who are in recovery call it—raising the bottom. It means that a person with the disease of alcoholism can be helped before he or she has lost everything. It doesn't mean the person hasn't experienced the years of denial, the destruction of personal relationships, the depths of despair and the utter self-loathing that are such a part of the disease. But it does mean the suffering likely has been interrupted long before it might have had the disease been allowed to run its course unchecked to jail, a hospital or a graveyard.

However and wherever the bottom came, whatever the circumstances or the stories of the people, one thing binds Cash and Jorgenson and Ford. They were alcoholics and had lost the power to control their drinking. Although very different in background, profession, and personality, each of them had reached a common point in their lives. They came to the point at which they could no longer deny the truth of their situation, which is described in the first step of the program of Alcoholics Anonymous: "We admitted we were powerless over alcohol, that our lives had become unmanageable."

Chapter Three

Surrender

People addicted to alcohol and other drugs can't weigh the consequences of their actions. They may be unable to see what their drinking or drug use is doing to them and, often, to those around them. That's
a common thread in the stories of those who are trying to recover from
chemical dependency.

Take country singer Larry Gatlin.

He was a smooth-voiced, good-looking singer and songwriter on
his way to the top as the front man for The Gatlin Brothers. His engaging
grin and curly hair were as well known to fans of country music, as was
his clear, strong tenor voice. He had talent, the right material and an excel-
lent group of musicians backing him on tour. Everything was going his
way, except his growing dependency on alcohol and cocaine.

Gatlin just wanted to fit in with the gang.

"I believe it all started the first night I got drunk. It felt good," Gatlin said in his interview for the television series *It's Great to be Alive*. He ran
with a crowd and hung around a lifestyle that seemed not only to condone
liquor and drug use but almost to expect it.

"You were supposed to get high and write these wonderful songs,"
he said. "We thought it was OK. My buddies were doing it…My heroes
were doing it."

He graduated to stronger drugs, especially cocaine, an alluring pow-
der of which Gatlin says, "I loved it. It felt good…for a while."

As he grew older, it took greater and greater quantities of cocaine to
get him high. He was mixing drugs too—as many users do—taking valium
and alcohol with the cocaine, adjusting his mood with the "uppers" that
got him going and the "downers" that brought him back to earth. Good
times made possible by chemistry.

But the good times ran out for Gatlin.

"I was sick all the time," he said. "I looked like a dead man. I didn't eat, didn't sleep."

He became extremely paranoid, an emotional effect often associated with heavy use of cocaine. He locked himself in his room, pulled the shades, wouldn't go out in public, feared people were out to get him.

"I didn't know who they were, but I knew they were out to get me," Gatlin said.

He recalls the turning point—a moment after a long, long period of partying when he regained consciousness to discover there were no more drugs. Somehow, he found himself staring in a mirror, and he despaired of what he'd become.

"It was the lowest moment of my life," Gatlin said. He fell to his knees. "I said, 'God, if you don't help me, I'm going to die.'"

After years of refusing to see how alcohol and drugs were ruining his life, Larry Gatlin had a moment of clarity during which his condition became reality.

"I think I had known it," he said later. "But I didn't know there were alternatives."

Many alcoholics find themselves at that moment of self-awareness, too, but it isn't always the end of their misery.

They may, in such moments of temporarily sober remorse, see with perfect clarity just how completely alcohol is ruining their lives. They may know full well that the next binge means they'll lose their spouse, their family and home. They may understand entirely that the next missed business meeting or the next drunken luncheon means they'll be out of a job. They may recognize that the money they're spending in a third-rate tavern on drinks they're buying for people they've never met before means they won't be able to make the car payment, write the mortgage check or buy shoes for the baby or food for the family.

Even if they know all those things, they sometimes still seem powerless to react sensibly. They can't just walk out of the tavern, or put down the glass after the first martini of the afternoon. It is the insanity of the disease that its victims repeat again and again a harmful behavior, believing the outcome will be different next time.

The nature of alcoholism is such that the alcoholic, by himself, almost never escapes.

He may know and accept that if he drinks, he dies. But he also is convinced, down to the deepest part of his being, that if he doesn't get another drink, he'll die anyway. That conflict tears the alcoholic apart. It destroys every aspect of his life, and it destroys the lives of the people around him.

But there is a way out. For two decades, many of those suffering alcoholics, especially those in the Upper Midwest, found the way out at a place called River Park. Jorgenson—with the help of others—developed the place. He designed its programs and made it a reality. He used the techniques and principles that worked in his own recovery, and he saw that they worked for thousands of others.

Jorgenson has never forgotten how he got from the despair of that lonely motel room to the promises of a life of sobriety and of striving to help others. His story is unique, yet those who've been able to start the process of recovery through treatment programs such as River Park's will be familiar with feelings and changes they themselves experienced.

What happens inside an alcoholic that turns him from a hopeless and helpless drunk into a functioning human being again? What miracle restores the power of choice to one who for so long has been able only to spin out of control, ever on the downward spiral of chemical dependency?

For sure it isn't will power. Take it from anyone who has been very long in recovery from alcoholism or drug abuse. With extremely rare exceptions, they agree that will power had nothing to do with it. Had it been will power, what one among them would have continued drinking after seeing the misery it was causing?

Certainly Glenn Jorgenson wouldn't have. Can anyone imagine he would have chosen willingly to continue his drinking and prescription drug use to the point at which it had cost him jobs and friendships, to the point at which it had put his marriage in jeopardy, to the point at which it had robbed him of his health, his emotional well-being, his self-respect and his very feeling of self-worth?

Can anyone doubt that, lying in that motel room, crying out to a God he had truly lost the ability to trust, can anyone doubt that Glenn Jorgenson would have given anything, would have gone to any length, to be freed of his demon? Of course not. He'd have done, said or given anything. The point is, he had nothing left to give or promise or do. Except this one thing—he could give himself.

In his anguished cry, "I'm finished," that's exactly what he did. He surrendered completely. He quit fighting, quit denying, quit pretending and quit holding up a shield to keep the world out. He simply gave up. He surrendered. In doing so, he saved his life.

That's an often-misunderstood concept in the journey of an alcoholic to sobriety, that business of surrender. We're raised to believe surrender is defeat, giving up is a sign of weakness. In breaking the cycle of chemical dependency, surrender is a prerequisite to victory, noted Garry Moore, veteran actor, television personality and recovering alcoholic, when he appeared on the *It's Great To Be Alive* program.

"You must first surrender before you can ever start to win the war against alcoholism," Moore said.

Dr. Dennis Waitley, a well-known expert in the field of alcoholism treatment, agrees.

"It's the toughest challenge of all, to accept the fact, to become aware in your own mind that you have a problem, and to accept the fact that you're going to do something about it," he said.

Glenn Jorgenson knew he had to do something about his drinking. He just couldn't conceive of anything that would work. He certainly didn't expect chemical-dependency treatment to work. That he agreed to let friends cart him off to a facility in Minnesota probably showed more than anything else in his life how hopelessly defeated he felt. He had nothing left, not even the strength to fight this last, great humiliation.

Ask recovering alcoholics why they went to treatment or started attending Alcoholics Anonymous meetings, and many of them will simply say, "I had no place else to go."

They'd run out of choices, and so had Jorgenson.

And so, he agreed to give treatment a try, scarcely daring to allow himself the smallest hope that it might help him.

✳ ✳ ✳

The early days of Jorgenson's treatment weren't easy.

Complete withdrawal from all alcohol and prescription drugs after decades of abuse meant an agony of physical reactions—aching joints and muscles, trembling nerves, chills, headaches. Sometimes in those first days and lonely nights, Jorgenson wondered if he'd live through it. Sometimes, right at first when withdrawal hurt the most, he wondered if he even wanted to.

But in the suffering, he found a strength he'd not tapped for years, one he barely knew he still had. For Jorgenson discovered this simple fact: He wanted to be well again. He wanted to be the functioning, productive and happy person he'd grown up believing he should be. He wanted, simply put, to live.

That lesson he learned on the fourth day of his treatment when he was put, quite by chance, to a horrible test. When he'd checked into the treatment center, his supply of pills and other prescription medications had been taken from him. He'd been terrified when that happened. He'd come to depend on those capsules and pills. He'd taken them for so long. How would he get through a day without them?

On that fourth day in treatment, he made an exhilarating yet frightening discovery. Digging in his suitcase for another shirt, he found a stash of pills. The nurse hadn't gotten the whole supply, after all. She probably thought she had. She'd taken away 17 different kinds of prescription drugs on the first day. Who would have imagined there'd be even more?

Yet right here, in the bottle Jorgenson lifted carefully out of the side pocket of his suitcase, was relief from the pain and the suffering.

Jorgenson had entered treatment during the period that Christians refer to as Holy Week, the time between Palm Sunday and Easter Sunday. It was Friday when he discovered the previously overlooked stash of pills—Good Friday, a day set aside to remember and reflect on Jesus Christ's time of prayer in the Garden of Gethsemane, on His trial and flogging and crucifixion at Calvary.

As Glenn Jorgenson held the bottle of pills in his palm, he faced his own version of Gethsemane. Although he knew the power the medication contained to bring temporary relief from his suffering, something deep within him warned against succumbing to the temptation of the quick fix. He put the pills back in his suitcase, snapped the clasps and shoved the luggage back in the closet.

All that evening, all through that long, tortured night, he argued with himself. Lying on sweat-soaked sheets on his cot, he stared across the room at the closet door. Open the door, and the shaking, the pain and the pure misery would be gone in a moment. And yet, something within him resisted. A hundred times, maybe more, he moved as if to rise and walk to the closet. Each time he hesitated, almost hearing a voice telling him the short path across this single room would lead to his complete ruin. A hundred times, maybe more, he lay back on his rumpled pillow, drew his knees to his chest and hugged himself tightly, as if he'd fly apart otherwise.

Sleep didn't come that night to Glenn Jorgenson. Neither did the relief from the physical and emotional pain, although he prayed again and again for that relief. Still, when the morning sun broke through a cottony layer of clouds that stretched low on the eastern horizon, a resolve had formed. He may not have gotten the prayed-for relief from the suffering, but he had gotten the strength to call the nurse and tell her she'd missed this one last bottle of pills during the admissions procedures.

The action didn't give Jorgenson any peace of mind—not right away, at least. In fact, as he reflects back on that long Good Friday night and the decision to give up his last supply of mood-altering drugs, he says, "I didn't look on it as having done anything noble. I was fully prepared to simply die there. It was as if some force had reached me for that one night and told me not to take the pills."

At the time, he was no different than most people in his understanding of how prescription medication works. He didn't know how addicting many prescription drugs can be. In the years that have passed since his treatment, Jorgenson has learned that some of the most difficult cases of addiction involve prescription drugs—legal medication that is being abused for the same relief and good feelings and the same escape that people seek when they drink in an alcoholic manner.

In alcohol programs, people like Jorgenson—hooked on both alcohol and drugs—are referred to as dually addicted. Their withdrawal is often more fierce than is that of the alcoholic alone or the drug addict alone. And the time it takes for their bodies, minds and emotions to return to some semblance of normal feeling is often much longer.

Looking back, Jorgenson can see clearly how true that is. At the time of his treatment, though, he believed alcohol was his problem. The pills just took away some of the hurt for a while.

And so, concentrating on the alcohol that had caused such misery in his once promising life, Glenn Jorgenson gave up. He faced himself honestly, perhaps for the first time in his life. He admitted the plain truth. He was an alcoholic.

That was the first step:

"We admitted we were powerless over alcohol, that our lives had become unmanageable."

Could any other 13 words in the world so aptly describe his condition, Jorgenson wondered.

"Powerless over alcohol?" How could he doubt it? How many more insane actions and decisions would be necessary to prove that one?

"Our lives had become unmanageable?" The most gifted debater, the skills of the most learned defense counsel couldn't put the lie to that phrase when examined in the context of the Jorgenson life.

And yet...

And yet, actually admitting he was an alcoholic didn't follow automatically. He fought the notion. He hated the very idea that it could be true of him. An alcoholic was the jailbird, the skid-row bum. An alcoholic was the gutter-dweller who moved from one dead-end job to the next.

The counselors at the treatment center agreed. Yes, those people indeed might be alcoholics, they said. So might a seemingly successful business leader who drank until he passed out, blacked out or was thrown out of the corner tavern every Friday and Saturday night. So might the housewife who drank secretly during the day and who greeted the children in a stupor at suppertime.

Alcohol, they told him, is no respecter of person. It doesn't pass over the churchgoer or the good looker or the genius. It crosses race, sex and class lines, and it kills people.

Comedian and television actor Dick Van Dyke expressed that truth when he appeared on *It's Great To Be Alive*.

"Anyone can become an alcoholic," Van Dyke said. "It doesn't matter whether he's successful. I didn't have any worries. Why did I drink? I didn't drink because I had worries. I drank because I was an alcoholic. I drank because I drank."

Actor Garry Moore laughingly told about the time, some years after he'd begun his recovery from alcoholism, when the daughter of a friend approached him for counseling. Moore related the story this way:

> "I remember getting a call from a young lady—she was about 35 years old. She called me up and said she thought perhaps she was an alcoholic. We discussed it, and I said. "Nobody can tell you you're an alcoholic unless you say to yourself, 'I am an alcoholic.'
>
> "Out of this discussion, we came to the conclusion that she was an alcoholic. She went home and told her mother (I've known her mother for years, a very dear friend of mine). Her daughter said, 'Garry and I talked it over, and I am an alcoholic, and I am going to do something about it.' Her mother called me up absolutely furious and said, 'My daughter cannot be an alcoholic. She was a debutante.'
>
> "That doesn't cut any ice. You can get just as drunk being a debutante as you can being anything else in the world."

Over time, Jorgenson learned this simple definition of alcoholism: "If you're having problems in any phase of your life and alcohol is involved, you're probably an alcoholic."

Early in treatment, though, even as the realization that he was indeed an alcoholic began to root itself firmly in Jorgenson's mind, his spirit fought the notion. Admitting that in the privacy of a small room in a sheltered treatment center was one thing. Saying it openly to others was something else again. Could he do that?

The program of Alcoholics Anonymous suggested that he must do that, if he would ever begin to make progress on the journey to recovery. The counselors at the treatment center agreed. It's a disease, they told him. It doesn't make you a bad person, not a weak-willed human being and certainly not an evil one. It only makes you a person who needs help to stop drinking. And admitting that the problem exists is the giant first step.

Even with their encouragement and understanding, Jorgenson felt humiliated the first time he stood in front of the other clients at the center and said, haltingly, "My name is Glenn Jorgenson, and I am an alcoholic."

In time, he would come to accept that phrase as easily as the first audience to whom he ever spoke it accepted the admission. The first few times he uttered it, though, he only felt shame.

Even that feeling of embarrassment didn't put Jorgenson in an exclusive club. Many, many alcoholics and addicts struggle mightily to admit their disease that first time. They've become so accustomed to considering the alcoholic a spineless and weak individual that it's hard to say the words that will put them on the road to recovery.

That message slowly began to sink in as Glenn Jorgenson's days in treatment passed. The small-town boy who'd always considered himself something of an oddity, who was never sure he quite fit in with the people around him unless he was drinking, discovered he wasn't alone at all. The treatment center was filled with other alcoholics—ministers, business leaders, laborers, and housewives. They shared a common problem, alcoholism. And they admitted it openly.

Jorgenson did, too,

"My name is Glenn, and I'm an alcoholic."

The awkward feeling each time he said those words began to disappear as the days passed. Gradually, instead of embarrassment, he began to feel a sense of hope as he spoke the sentence. Perhaps it would be possible to lead a normal life without the alcohol and without the pills, he thought. Others seemed to be able to do it. Clients came and went nearly every day, the 30-day veterans lugging their suitcases out the door to be replaced by trembling, pale newcomers.

Watching uncertain, hopeless alcoholics change into sober, seemingly confident men and women during the course of their treatment, Jorgenson started to feel an optimism he'd not experienced for years.

It didn't come easily. His body, strung out by the harsh withdrawal from a potpourri of prescription drugs and booze, was weak and shaky. His nerves were raw. His sleep pattern was uneven, a mix of short, restless periods of unconsciousness followed by long stretches of troubled insomnia.

Even so, he managed to absorb enough of the treatment program's mix of readings, lectures and group discussions to begin to believe that he might be able to take this new beginning and make it a meaningful life. And, even in those early, hesitant days of sobriety, he began to wonder if his life shouldn't have more of a purpose than it had had.

Again and again, he read the second and third steps of the AA program.

Step Two: Came to believe that a power greater than ourselves could restore us to sanity.

Step Three: Made a decision to turn our will and our lives over to God, as we understood him.

The second step made sense to Jorgenson. How could it not, given his personal experience of having been lifted from a hopeless, helpless state and offered a chance to reclaim his life?

To the depth of his soul Glenn Jorgenson understood that he'd been powerless in the presence of alcohol. Should he doubt it for a single moment, he had only to flash back on the last, horrible day in the motel room in Pierre. No human being would choose to end up in that place and in that condition. Indeed, he was powerless over alcohol. And, indeed, his life had become unmanageable.

As he reflected on his time in treatment, and particularly as he relived that long Good Friday night when he wrestled with himself and his personal demons before turning that last stash of prescription medication over to the nursing staff, Jorgenson also began to believe that he'd been touched by a Higher Power.

The Big Book spoke of a spiritual experience. Had that been what was happening in the pre-Easter night when Jorgenson struggled so desperately against the lure of the pills? Hesitantly, almost fearfully, he was coming to believe that a power greater than himself could restore him to sanity.

Ah, but with that belief came a certain responsibility. For, if Glenn Jorgenson had, indeed, been given another chance at life, what was he to make of this new opportunity?

It certainly seemed to be the case that his life had been touched by a spiritual force. He who was once hopeless suddenly had hope. He who'd been helpless now was able to function, if only in a few, simple things. Something had happened in his life, and he'd been changed. His life had been saved.

Why?

The question began to gnaw at him. Why? If there is a Higher Power—and Glenn Jorgenson believed such a Power existed—then why was he spared?

There could be only one reason. God had a plan for his life. He must turn his will and his life over to God and ask for guidance in the remaining days of his existence. He couldn't see the shape of this master plan that had been created for his life, but he came to believe with all his heart that such a plan existed. In his readings, he happened on a short, lovely prayer that helped him express his feelings at that time.

In AA, it's called the Third Step Prayer, and it says simply:

"God, I offer myself to thee, to build with me and to do with me as Thou wilt. Relieve me of the bondage of self, that I may better do Thy will. Take away my difficulties, that victory over them will bear witness, to

those I would help, of Thy love, Thy power and Thy way of life. May I do
Thy will always."

It's impossible to overstate how important the attitude embodied in
that prayer was for Jorgenson. It marked a most amazing reversal of the
way he approached life.

A man of much self-sufficiency, he'd not had to rely on anyone.
Others relied on him. A man of little patience, he'd seldom waited willingly for anything in his life. He'd always wanted what he wanted and when
he wanted it. A man of considerable selfishness, he'd always believed, un-
consciously, perhaps, but with fervor nonetheless, that it was his will that
should be done. To reach a point in his life at which he was able to pray
earnestly to do God's will was a remarkable piece of growth.

The decision to seek God's will helped Jorgenson make it through
the rest of his time in treatment. He still suffered daily symptoms of withdrawal from two decades of drugs and alcohol. He still rode a rollicking
roller coaster of rapidly changing feelings as his emotions tried to adjust to
the lack of artificial stimulation for the first time in years.

Too shaky to trust himself to drive back to Pierre, he asked his
brother to come and get him when his treatment period had ended. He
left the Minnesota center still praying daily, still asking and wondering for
what purpose he'd been spared.

The answer, when it finally came, made more sense than anything
he'd ever known before in his life.

Chapter Four

Home Again

G lenn Jorgenson returned to his home and family a changed man, yet still filled with an inner conflict.

He wanted desperately to continue the recovery he'd begun in the Minnesota treatment center. He accepted his alcoholism and felt he had started to gain an understanding, at least a little bit, of the nature of the disease.

At the same time, he experienced moments of fear. Could he really make the progress he wanted? What would happen when he returned to the old gang, the old hometown, the proximity of so many of his drinking hangouts and comrades?

The conflict he felt upon returning home didn't have hopelessness about it. It made him feel, well, unsettled, or perhaps incomplete. It was as if he'd been given a list of chores to do around the house and yard for the weekend and had misplaced the list while his labor was only half done. Somewhere in his life, Jorgenson could feel unfinished business. It was waiting to be taken care of, if only he could identify what it was he needed to do.

It wasn't easy, either, to walk in the front door of his home that first time after treatment. To say Jorgenson had been apprehensive about his homecoming would be to understate the turmoil he felt.

He wondered how Phyllis would react, how the two girls would treat him, what they made of his sudden absence and now his abrupt return. He was unsure if his strict, conservative parents would ever understand how his life had gotten into such a turmoil and how determined he was to change that with the way he'd spend the remaining years in sobriety.

He had little to fear, as it turned out, although Phyllis and his parents all seemed to hover a lot, at first. They moved around him quietly, as if a firm step on the carpeted floor would send a foot crashing through into the basement.

That was a bit unsettling, but not unexpected. After all, he'd returned a seemingly different man. Phyllis, especially, could sense the change, yet who could blame her for having doubts? How many times in the past had he promised her he'd change one behavior or another? How many times had he said he'd meet her someplace, then failed to show up? How often had he stayed overlong at happy hour, breezing into the house to find supper long past and Phyllis hurt and angry?

He wanted to tell her those days were all over now. Things were different now. He was different. But he knew the only sure way to tell her how much he'd changed would be with his actions. He realized that it would take an unflagging commitment to living the principles of this new life he'd been introduced to in treatment. It would take constant, conscientious follow-through on every promise, no matter how unimportant.

Put in simplest terms, it would take hard work, and time.

In spite of her unspoken reservations, Phyllis readily accepted him back into their home. His two daughters, once the initial excitement of the homecoming had passed, quickly and rather casually returned to their individual and shared interests. It pleased him in a way that they showed so little interest in his absence.

At the same time, if the truth be told, it upset him just a little for a moment. He'd been through perhaps the most dramatic few weeks in his entire life, and his own children acted as if he'd just popped around the corner for a loaf of bread.

He reminded himself that if, in fact, the two girls had escaped relatively unscathed from his extended period of substance abuse, that was something to be enormously grateful for and reason to thank a Higher Power for helping him to begin recovery when he did.

His parents seemed uncertain about the whole business of alcoholism, although they offered immediate and unconditional support for him in his determination to grow in sobriety.

"I'd been thinking that talking to them about my experience with alcohol and my treatment would be a tremendously difficult thing to do,"

Jorgenson recalls. "Instead, it was really quite a positive thing. My mom
didn't understand what alcoholism was really about, I guess, but she loved
me and wanted anything that would be good for me, for Phyllis and the
girls. My dad, I don't think he really understood this disease either—not
completely—but he was accepting and supportive. He also made an effort
to learn more about alcoholism, and he eventually became one of the
most popular lecturers that River Park ever had."

Jorgenson soon discovered that other people in his life were equally
accepting of the changes he was trying to make.

One of his first calls outside the immediate family was to his hometown banker. It was a visit Jorgenson dreaded.

"We still owned some property, but I'd lost some money I borrowed,
and I had to begin finding a way to square that," he says. "The banker
seemed willing to work with me, and that was terribly important at the
time. Remember, I didn't have any real idea of what I wanted to do with
my life. I'd always been pretty successful at finding positions and making
career moves that allowed me to take care of my family and invest some
money, too. But somehow those kinds of jobs just didn't have the attraction anymore, not the way they did before I began to work on my program
of recovery."

It would be several months before that feeling of having some unfinished business began to shape itself into an idea, a way of life and a way
to give to others some of the good things he'd been given himself.

In the meantime, he set about the business of making some amends
to people he'd injured, insulted or ignored during his long period of drinking. The process was slow at times. He often had to pray for the courage
to face people whose trust he'd once had, whose trust he'd shattered by
his drinking behavior. He talked with the banker, with employers and
business partners, with the friend who'd given him that one last chance at
a job.

In each case the results were surprisingly positive. The blue book
of Alcoholics Anonymous had suggested that such would be the case.
If amends were honestly offered, with a sincere desire and an apology
for past actions, words or behavior, the most likely outcome would be a

wholehearted acceptance, the book had said. But it's one thing to read such things in a book, another to discover face-to-face the absolute truth of the words.

With each such encounter, Jorgenson felt his spirits lift a little more. He learned valuable lessons with every amending encounter, not the least of which was that he could depend on the Serenity Prayer to quiet his nerves and bolster his courage.

That short prayer, recited at the beginning of most meetings of Alcoholics Anonymous, gives a simple perspective to a human being's place in the universe.

"God," the prayer says, "grant me the serenity to accept the things I cannot change, courage to change the things I can and the wisdom to know the difference."

Jorgenson recalled, "I was saying the Serenity Prayer almost constantly in those early days. I maybe began using it as a way to ask for courage, or strength to do the things I thought I needed to do. As I repeated it, though, I gained a greater appreciation for the patience that is implicit in the first phrase, the serenity to accept things I couldn't do anything about."

Further repetition of the prayer led Jorgenson to an even greater appreciation of the power of the last phrase, he said.

"I really became struck by that, the wisdom to know," he said. "I began to understand that if it were possible that I could always know which situations or people or circumstances I could do something about and which ones I could no nothing about, my life would be much simpler. That doesn't mean it would be easy. I might have to work very hard at acceptance and at courage. But I wouldn't waste as much time trying to change things that I couldn't, and I might be quicker to pray for courage to change things I could. The wisdom to know the difference became a central part of my daily prayer."

Other people's actions and feelings were things Jorgenson came to see he could do nothing about except live the way he believed God wanted him to live. That realization brought a sense of freedom, he said.

"It came in such simple ways, sometimes," Jorgenson said. "I so dreaded my first trip back up to the Capitol Building to join the coffee crowd in the cafeteria. I felt as if everyone's eyes were on my every action, and I tried to be nonchalant as I fetched my cup and saucer."

Of course he spilled his coffee, dropping the cup and saucer with a crash in the middle of the cafeteria. Embarrassing as that moment was, it wasn't fatal.

"It was just one, tiny moment," Jorgenson says. "I'd missed the table with my cup and saucer. And when I looked around, I realized most of the people in that room weren't paying any attention to me anyway. They had their own lives and I wasn't the most important thing in their world."

In that early period of sobriety, Jorgenson's days consisted of searching—for a job that seemed to offer the fulfillment he couldn't quite identify but knew he wanted, and for the guidance to make each day meaningful.

"I meditated quite a lot, trying as sincerely as I knew how to ask for direction," he says. "That long Good Friday night in treatment remained vivid in my mind. The feeling that I had a purpose to serve—if I could only be wise enough to see what it was—sometimes overwhelmed me."

* * *

The city of Pierre is built into the bluffs of the Missouri River. It's nestled on the inside curve of a spot where the river—having run nearly straight south from the point where it passes into the state from North Dakota—makes a gentle bend and meanders in a haphazard, southeasterly direction. The river is wide in its downstream reach from Pierre, and on calm days, it lies flat as a tabletop and reflects the blue of the sky.

About a dozen miles southeast of the town, a highway rest stop and picnic area is built atop a modest bluff on the north bank of the Missouri. Jorgenson, who filled some of his first, uncertain days at home after treatment with long automobile drives through the countryside around Pierre, discovered this riverside observation point early one restless morning.

In the days that followed, he came to the spot often, as many as three, four or five times a day. He parked his car and sat for long, quiet stretches, letting the expanse of gently flowing river and the calming movement of the green prairie grasses lull him into a contemplative state, half dreaming, half praying.

The greatest emotional upset couldn't last long against the spell of the still water and green pastures that Jorgenson began to link with the 23rd Psalm. Sometimes he'd drive to the overlook as eagerly as if he were on his way to a spiritual gathering. Stopping the car, he'd read from the book of daily meditations that was his constant companion. Then he'd pray the Serenity Prayer and the Lord's Prayer. After that, he'd often recite silently the peaceful words of the psalm this place so reminded him.

"The Lord is my shepherd, I shall not want. In green pastures he gives me repose. Beside the still waters he leads me. He refreshes my soul…"

That's how the 23rd Psalm begins, and that's how Jorgenson came to think of his time on the scenic overlook on the Missouri River. That the words and the meaning of the psalm came to play such an integral part in the location, formal name and philosophy of River Park when that treatment center was eventually started is no accident.

The times of prayer and meditation beside the still waters and surrounded by the green pastures were slowly changing Glenn Jorgenson into a man who would be in the right condition to see his destiny and accept the challenges and opportunities it offered.

✳ ✳ ✳

It's often said that God works through human beings to effect positive changes in the world, and that was true in Jorgenson's post-treatment life.

Among the friends with whom he shared coffee on an almost daily basis were two or three who understood how widespread alcoholism was in the community, the state and the nation. They understood the need for more treatment opportunities, and morning after morning they kicked around ideas about how to meet that need.

Alcoholics Anonymous and its philosophy—a one-to-one approach of one drunk helping another—were the bedrocks of recovery from chemical dependency, these people knew. But how to reach the many people who needed help?

Over the steaming black coffee, Jorgenson's friends, especially two men named Shanard Burke and Jack Parr, brainstormed ways to get help more quickly to more people, and maybe to get the help to them before they'd lost everything in their lives.

Burke and Parr had, in 1968, formed a corporation called River Park. Their intention was to start a halfway house for women recovering from alcoholism, and the Benedictine Sisters at St. Mary's Hospital had offered to let them use part of their convent for the project.

The need certainly existed, they said. Perhaps some funding might be available through one or another of the government agencies that offered planning grants.

Burke and Parr put the idea to Jorgenson one morning. Would he be willing to work on such a proposal, researching the need, writing the grant applications, refining their coffee-shop conversation into something that might stand a chance of being considered seriously by a government agency? After all, they told Jorgenson, his years of experience working with state agencies and personnel policies had been the ideal background for spearheading this project.

Jorgenson agreed to work on the plans for a while. "I said, yes, I'll do this until I know more about what I'm going to be doing for a career from now on."

So Jorgenson began thinking of ways to put together a treatment center to help alcoholics. But he didn't consider this his life's mission, not at first. It was something that offered the potential of helping many people, if it ever became a reality. That possibility gave Jorgenson a good feeling. Working on this project would be one way to repay the debt he'd felt he owed to a Higher Power ever since the night in treatment when he made a decision to live a life of helping others.

He still needed to find a real job, he believed. He had requests out in many areas. It was just a matter of time before he'd find something that would keep his family fed, clothed and sheltered and still be spiritually rewarding. He was looking. And when the right thing came along, he'd recognize it.

He did, too, although not in the way he'd ever dreamed he would.

A job offer did come through one day. It was a good job, with the Equal Employment Opportunity Commission. The work was nothing he couldn't handle. The salary would support his family. But it would mean a move to Kansas City, and neither Jorgenson nor Phyllis were too excited about the idea of leaving Pierre. The community had been the site of many of their worst heartbreaks, but they'd had an incredible number of good times there, too, good memories, good friends and the promise of a good future with the right job.

Jorgenson turned the EEOC offer over and over in his mind, even as he thought often about ways to make the proposed alcoholism treatment center plan a reality. He prayed and meditated, visited the river bluff often and talked with Phyllis late into the evenings. Time after time he asked God for guidance. How could he know for sure that what he might do would be God's will for him? If only he could get a clear sign of which way to go, he'd throw himself wholeheartedly into the effort.

The sign, when it came, was so dramatic he could scarcely believe his senses.

It came while he was on a trip to Rapid City, the state's second largest city that is built at the very edge of the Black Hills of western South Dakota. The two-lane highway between Pierre and Rapid City in those days dipped and climbed across the rolling prairie. Giant wheat fields stretched off to the horizon, interrupted sometimes by short-grass pastures holding herds of white-faced Hereford cattle. The towns were small and widely spaced, sometimes 25 or 30 miles apart. On any typical weekday, the road belonged to a few state workers and traveling sales people, a school bus or two and farmers in pickups or on tractors pulling mowers and combines from field to field.

A person alone in a vehicle could lose himself in contemplation of problems. On that decisive day, Jorgenson did just that.

"I was deep in thought, weighing the Kansas City position, trying to think of any job leads I might have overlooked in the Pierre area, and always somewhere in the back of my mind working over the notion of alcoholism and the needs in that field," Jorgenson said. "Quite without warning, I heard a voice. It wasn't audible, exactly, yet it was as if God was in the car. The message was clear as a bell. It said, 'I want you to stay in Pierre and build a center.'"

Jorgenson found a roadside approach and pulled his car off the highway for a moment. The message remained as clear and as strong inside the vehicle as if the words were being spoken aloud. He started the car, turned around in the highway and hurried back to Pierre. Parking the car in his driveway at home, Jorgenson rushed into the house and hugged Phyllis.

"I'm not going to take the Kansas City job," he told her excitedly. "We're going to stay here in Pierre. I know now what it is that I'm supposed to do."

Chapter Five

A Purpose

Ever since Jack Parr and Shanard Burke had started raising questions about the possibility that their dreamed-of half-way house might be located in an unoccupied convent attached to St. Mary's Hospital in Pierre, Jorgenson had, almost without knowing it, been linking the words river and park. It was almost as if, like the voice on the highway he would hear just a few short weeks later, this one special name had been whispered to him from somewhere deep in his subconscious.

River Park.

The convent that Shanard and Jack were so excited about was available for sale or lease. Along with the adjoining hospital, its brick walls formed the northern border of a tree-shaded city park. The park's southern boundary was the sandy shore of the Missouri River.

The river, the park and River Park.

The green pastures and still waters of the 23rd Psalm, the images Jorgenson saw so vividly and so frequently from his scenic overlook just downstream from this place. Those same things were right here, just two blocks from his own home, in a location that his friends believed would be perfect for the halfway house they desperately wanted to construct.

Someday, and sooner than Jorgenson could have imagined at the time, this would be the foundation of River Park.

But that would come only after a lot of legwork had been done, mostly by Jorgenson. Being the one without a steady job, he had the time to ask the questions and make some preliminary plans and chase down possible sources of grant money to see if such a venture was even possible.

Jorgenson admitted later than when his friends first began talking about the idea that the convent could become a functioning halfway house, he had his doubts. He even recalled drawing a huge laugh from his coffee-shop pals when, hearing them talk about a Benedictine order of nuns, he casually remarked that he had always thought Benedictine was an after-dinner drink, often accompanied by brandy.

The more he listened, though, the more excited Jorgenson became. He began to ask around. His friend Ben Hins, director of the South Dakota Department of Vocational Rehabilitation, had grant money available for a feasibility study of the idea, if local organizers could raise $450 in matching money. Shanard's father kicked in the first $50, and Jorgenson tapped as many old contacts as he could think of to scrape together the rest of the necessary matching funds.

Writing the proposal for the center, Jorgenson discovered that his past experience in state government had given him a unique combination of sources of information and a solid understanding of how the bureaucracy functioned and how a skilled person could work through and around it to get budget figures and health reports and background data that would form the core of the study.

"This turned out to be a pretty important time for me," Jorgenson recalled. "I was staying sober, and I was incredibly grateful for that. But there were a lot of rough days in that early recovery, and it was a little unsettling not to know what I was going to do career-wise. I certainly didn't come out of treatment with this tremendous idea of starting a center out in the middle of South Dakota. But research and planning and writing, those were things I felt pretty confident I could do."

So, he headed for the state library and checked out as much material as he could find on the subject of alcoholism. He took the books and periodicals and studies and reports to a long table, sat down, opened the first book and began to learn about the disease he shared with hundreds of thousands of others in the country.

One of the first things he learned was that the alcoholism problem in South Dakota was much more widespread than he'd dreamed. Hard facts seemed not to exist, and nobody seemed to be interested in measuring the exact nature of the problem. Even so, the anecdotal material available and the reports on the frequency of drunken driving and bar fights and broken homes showed Jorgenson that abuse of alcohol was pervasive in his home state.

Another important finding was that state government was ill equipped to respond to the needs of the alcoholic. The state lacked the money and the manpower to attack the problem, and even if those had existed, it lacked a clear sense of mission that this was an area in which government should be involved.

Jorgenson became terribly discouraged early in the process when he realized that the dream of a halfway house for women would be almost impossible to realize. South Dakota wasn't ready for such a thing when it lacked, for the most part, the basic treatment facilities and programs for the actively drinking alcoholic. Programs such as the one Jorgenson had attended in neighboring Minnesota were beginning to spring up across the country, but only by ones and twos and generally in the most heavily populated areas.

It simply wasn't good enough, Jorgenson said to himself. Then he said it to his friends Shanard and Jack.

They agreed, and the focus of their talks began gradually to change from a halfway house to the possibility of a primary alcoholism treatment facility. Suddenly, Jorgenson found himself in charge of writing a federal grant proposal for the start-up costs of an in-patient treatment center. For all the experience he'd had with government and with writing, this was a daunting situation. Nothing to do but start and see what happened, he decided.

"One of the things I'd been told again and again in treatment, and it's one of the first things anyone who goes to AA hears or sees written on the wall, is 'Keep it simple,'" Jorgenson said. "That's what I decided to try to do. And, really, when you look back over the years, so much of what made River Park so effective was the common sense we tried to use for every situation or problem. The disease is incredible; treatment and recovery can often seem very complicated; but at the heart of it all, we have to keep it simple."

That's what Jorgenson did.

"At first, the enormity of the job overwhelmed me," Jorgenson recalls. "I remember thinking to myself, 'Oh, God, how do I put this thing together?'" But, with a prayer for guidance and a willingness to tackle something he wasn't sure he could accomplish, he sat down at his desk.

"Once I sat down, I just started writing," he says. "It all came out. It was there in my mind or my soul. I can't say where it came from, but it came. It was only maybe nine or 10 sheets of paper, but there it was."

All but ignoring the stacks of books and journals he'd collected in his research, Jorgenson wrote. In one passionate, exhausting sitting, he finished the draft of a plan that would carry the futures of countless alcoholics. When he'd run out of things to say, he set his pen aside and leaned back in his chair, almost frightened by the simplicity of the plan he'd described for alcohol treatment.

What would the bureaucrats make of this? The heart of a plan for a comprehensive treatment program for alcoholics in ten short pages? They were used to pages of proposals, stacks of supporting documentation, a blizzard of words and paper. Would they take it seriously?

"Looking back, I can see that virtually everything we did at River Park was contained in that first plan," Jorgenson says. "So much of what River Park was all about was really common sense. But at the time we were trying to get started, there wasn't a whole lot of common sense in the field of alcoholism treatment."

With a prayer of thanks for having finished the proposal and a fervent, "Thy will be done," Jorgenson took the thin document to Ben Hins, who took it to the federal Vocational Rehabilitation office in Denver.

"I really was struggling to maintain a positive attitude," Jorgenson says. "I had the feeling this document contained the seed of perhaps the most important program I'd ever have a chance to be involved in. It felt right when I reviewed what I'd written. But getting someone else to see that? I just didn't know if that would come through. I knew I'd done my level best, and I'd asked for guidance from a Higher Power. I knew that was all I could do. But, yes, I still was nervous."

As it turned out, he had nothing to fear.

With a most un-bureaucratic speed, the agency approved the proposal. The grant was his. Nothing stood in the way of Jorgenson and his small band of big dreamers and the beginning of a central South Dakota in-patient treatment center for alcoholics. Nothing except…

What would they do next? What would they do now? Acceptance of the proposal seemed to be a sign that the federal agency thought the idea made sense and could be accomplished.

OK. How?

Jorgenson had been so busy putting his ideas and dreams into the plan, he really hadn't dwelled much on the consequences of success. It meant he'd have to forge ahead and try to put walls and a roof around the idea.

"I was almost floored by the realization that this dream could come true only if a lot of hard work went into building the center," he said. "Up to that time, it had been a wonderful thing to think about, a fantastic concept well worth the time and money it would take to create. All of a sudden, though, it was more than that. It was possible. It was expected to be completed. It was just up to those of us who had talked about it so much to get it done."

As he'd done so often during moments of stress, doubt or need since he'd emerged from treatment, Jorgenson's first action was to find a quiet place and a proper time to give thanks for the blessing of the Denver decision.

Now, at this time, Jorgenson still wasn't thinking about being the one to run River Park for the long haul. He was a businessman, after all, a politician, not some kind of social worker.

That experience with the voice on the road to Rapid City had made him stop and think, though. And, once he'd decided he was to make his home in Pierre, it was only a small step from his living room to the main office at River Park. Shanard Burke gave him a push.

"Why don't you run the center?" he asked when Jorgenson told him of his decision to remain in Pierre. "Why don't you be the one to run River Park?"

Jack Parr agreed, and when Jorgenson asked Phyllis what she thought of the suggestion, she simply smiled, hugged him warmly and said, "Did it ever occur to you that may have been what the voice on the highway was telling you?"

So, with another prayer for guidance on the new road he was about to travel, Jorgenson and Phyllis sat down together to begin planning the details of a treatment center. Glenn called his friend Lynn Carroll, who had founded in Minnesota the nation's first private non-profit treatment center, and Carroll agreed to help them as a consultant and lecturer. Questions and problems, decisions and solutions sometimes seemed to pile around them like elm leaves on a windy October afternoon.

Jorgenson quickly got into the habit of pausing at each new step, reflecting quietly on the next thing that needed to be done, and asking himself if it felt like the right thing.

"Someone once told me that to do good things in life, you need to pray as if everything depends on God and work as if it all depends on you," he said later. "That really was the way we approached all of this."

Jorgenson and Phyllis worked together to order supplies—sheets, towels, coffee makers, dressers, notebooks, and pencils. What about a refrigerator for the day room? Where do you find sturdy, comfortable beds at a reasonable price? Should there be a supply of any kinds of medicine? Medicine? Mercy, the place will need a nurse of some kind. How does a person go about hiring a nurse? What kind of carpet will stand up to the daily wear of 20 or 30 people and still look elegant and home-like? Who handles garbage pickup? What about plumbing? Is the wiring OK?

Somehow, even when it appeared that the latest problem with remodeling had them licked, a solution would present itself. Jorgenson particularly remembers that when they decided to install air conditioning in the old convent, a recovering alcoholic helped make sure the necessary work was finished.

Phyllis quit her job with state government to join Jorgenson in the daily work, becoming a laundress, cleaning woman and personal secretary. Anything that needed to be done that no one else was doing, Phyllis would tackle.

The Benedictine Sisters had moved from the convent to other nearby housing, and at first they had been a bit uncertain what to make of this flurry of activity with the aim of building a treatment center. It wasn't long, though, before several of them had joined enthusiastically into the effort, volunteering long and late hours to clean floors and hang curtains.

"I never will forget the sight of a couple of the Sisters hanging out the upper story windows, with cleaner and rags, just polishing those window panes until they sparkled in the sunlight," Jorgenson said. "There was no task they were reluctant to take on, and their cheerful work attitude inspired all of us who were involved."

Jorgenson had definite plans about the approach he intended to use toward treatment in River Park, and he had equally strong feelings about the physical surroundings that would be necessary to create the atmosphere that would give alcoholics who came to the center the best possible chance of recovery.

The carpet was to be shag (the style at the time), the colors of the walls and curtains rich if subdued. The furniture had to be comfortable and of good quality. Paintings would line the walls; plants would decorate spare corners and window ledges. The crowning touch, according to many who found their sobriety in the comforting rooms of River Park, would be the placement of oversized rocking chairs of strong, dark wood in each client room.

"Those rocking chairs were almost an off-hand decision, in a way," Jorgenson said. "The act of rocking always seemed to be such a soothing thing, and even the presence of a sturdy old rocker sitting near the bed, well, a lot of our early clients told me when they were finishing their treatment that the chair was one of the things that really reached out to them in their first days. Somehow, it was kind of a symbol of caring. It was one of the smartest things we did in decorating, I know that."

The top-of-the-line approach offended some people in South Dakota in the early days. Their idea of alcohol treatment seemed to be of an austere place with cots bolted to the floors, meager mattresses with thin, cheap blankets and metal, unbreakable chairs and desks.

"I wanted to make sure that the first impression each of these alcoholics received when they came through our door was that we cared enough about them to put out the good dishes, so to speak," Jorgenson said.

That message was to be central to River Park's success. It had to be conveyed in every aspect of the center, not only the furniture in the rooms, but the attitudes of the counselors, the demeanor of the receptionists and the way clients were treated in individual counseling sessions, in groups and in informal free time. That was to be the staff's approach in every encounter with a client. It was also to be the staff's approach to interactions with each other. And, even more significantly, it was to be the clients' approach in relationships among themselves.

Alcoholics and addicts had enough problems to deal with in their search for recovery. The soul-searching and sharing that would be expected of them would hardly be encouraged by an aloof or judgmental staff.

"Somewhere in my own recovery, I'd come across a bit of philosophy that perfectly explained what we were trying to do at River Park," Jorgenson said. "It said, 'Treat a man as he is, and he will remain as he is. Treat a man as he could be, and he will become the man he could be.' That's all we were trying to do."

Finally, the rooms were ready. The air-handling system worked, the carpet was raked bare of footprints. The staff had been hired. The counselors were, like Jorgenson, recovering alcoholics.

"You couldn't do now what we did in those days," Jorgenson said. "Now, we'd be required to have counselors with advanced degrees in social work or psychology or counseling. When River Park opened, our people had the qualifications that we believed were most important. They knew what it was like to be a drunk and what it was like to recover, and they cared deeply about the people who'd be coming to this place for help."

Attitude was critical to getting the center's program off to the right start.

Father Joseph Martin, a Catholic priest who lectured nationwide on alcoholism, says an alcoholic generally gets only two reactions from the rest of the population.

"He's either given preaching or he's shunned completely," the priest said during a visit to River Park in1978.

Father Martin also said attitude governs action, and most people judge an alcoholic by his behavior. That makes for some pretty harsh judgments. "Alcoholic behavior is always obnoxious, and we judge accordingly," Father Martin said. Those trying to help should ask one question before they judge, he suggested.

"Would anyone in his right mind do this?" he asked. "He can't be in his right mind and go to his mother's funeral drunk...He's not in his right mind."

Counselors and nurses at River Park, as well as any other staff members who might come in contact with clients, needed to be capable of setting aside any judgments and dealing with the person instead of the actions. For the most part, Jorgenson was able to find and hire men and women more than capable of doing just that.

A real find before the center opened had been one of the nuns, Sister Joyce Piatz. A nutritionist by education and training, she became a tireless worker, an energetic cheerleader and a voice of common-sense solutions to any problem.

Her value to the new center called River Park was foreshadowed on the opening day of treatment, Jorgenson recalls.

Once a treatment center is ready to open, it needs that one essential ingredient—a handful of alcoholics who want to change their lives. Jorgenson worked several contacts in the state to identify and contact seven such people.

The results were both instantaneous and daunting.

"A marvelous man named Doug Hudson worked to get some of these people to agree to try our treatment program, and he got together the God-awful-est collection of folks you'd ever imagine," Jorgenson recalled. "There were two carloads of them, seven people, most of whom had really been through the mill in their drinking lives. Those cars pulled up in the parking lot at River Park, and I confess I had a moment there when I wondered if we could help."

Standing with Sister Joyce at the window, looking out at the men and women who would become the first class at River Park, Jorgenson was hit suddenly with doubt. Although his every action for months and months had been geared toward this moment when the first clients would arrive for the help he knew the program could offer, he hadn't considered how desperately those people would need help. What if it didn't work this first time?

He remembers stepping back from the window, turning toward the center of the room and whispering, "Oh, God, what do we do now?"

That was the moment, he says, when he began to really appreciate the wisdom of the old AA slogans, such as "First things first" and "Keep it simple."

Sister Joyce reminded him of the need to look at the basics first, and she made him realize what a treasure she would be for the center and its clients.

"What do we do now?" she asked. "Why, we feed them."

Chapter Six

Beginning

As would prove to be the case time after time during River Park's eventful life, Sister Joyce had just the right suggestion.

Feed them. Of course.

The ensuing 30 days of treatment would involve an incredible amount of effort on the part of each of the seven suffering souls. They couldn't know it as they walked into the center for the first time, but they'd be tested in mind and body and spirit by the time they walked back out.

That first class of River Park clients hardly knew what to think as they met Jorgenson, Phyllis, Sister Joyce, Lloyd Jorgenson (Glenn's father) and Lynn Carroll for the first time. One or two of the men and women had been in treatment of one kind or another, but it hadn't much resembled the center they were seeing this time. One or two had been in jail, in the drunk tank, in shelters and detox centers and even psychiatric wards when everyone around them had finally thrown their hands in the air in despair and exclaimed, "He must be crazy, because nobody would act this way in his right mind."

As much as the pleasant, elegant surroundings in the center, the clients noticed this right away: When they walked in the door, nobody from the staff rushed to lock it behind them. That was a policy that would exist for the entire time River Park treated alcoholics. It was a very calculated and deliberate decision on Jorgenson's part, designed to convey the message that help was available, that he and the other staff members cared a great deal that the clients were there, but that each individual had a choice every day about whether to stay or leave.

"It was one of the things we did that really showed we were going to treat the clients with respect and with a high degree of trust," Jorgenson said. "A lot of places weren't doing that at the time."

No, they weren't. And, as with so many of the innovative approaches Jorgenson and his River Park program used, plenty of people were around to warn him that an unlocked treatment center simply wouldn't work.

"First time one of those alcoholics in there gets a hankering for a drink, he'll be out that door and gone," Jorgenson was told. Even some of Jorgenson's friends said an open door policy wouldn't work.

But with a few exceptions, the policy did work.

Jorgenson's staff described for each new client the campus boundaries they were expected to respect—a certain line of hedges in the park outside, the front door of the center and a limited area of the grounds that surrounded the hospital complex. No fences marked the boundaries; no white lines were painted in the grass or on the sidewalks. The limits were matter-of-factly laid out, just another way of treating people the way you'd expect them to act.

"It was an informal honor system, which was pretty unheard of in those days when you were dealing with a bunch of people whose lives had become just a long, endless string of breaking trust and going back on promises," Jorgenson said. "To have someone trust them, well, it was a pretty important step for most of our newcomers."

In the early days of River Park, Jorgenson and his staff did all sorts of things that other centers hadn't tried and that a small band of naysayers were convinced wouldn't be successful.

One of Jorgenson's truly important decisions was to not seek or accept federal or state grants. And except for that first matching grant for the feasibility study and another small grant for start-up costs, River Park operated without government funding.

"I knew in the deepest spot in my heart that the success of the program depended on me being able to decide how to approach treatment, based on my own experiences, my research and, most of all, guidance through prayer," Jorgenson said. "I'd been around enough government programs and agencies to know that if they start to help you with funding, it won't be long before they're the ones calling the shots on how you spend the money and how you run your program. There were plenty of times in the early days when we weren't generating much revenue and it would have been awfully easy to take the money. But I'm still firmly convinced that the policy not to do that was one of the reasons we were able to run the kind of program we did and to have the kind of successes we had. A number of treatment programs that followed us did get involved in that kind of funding, and eventually they suffered for it."

Jorgenson's funding policy perhaps cost him some contacts with government agencies that dealt with alcohol and drug programs in South Dakota. It wasn't playing by the same rules other centers followed, after all. River Park was being, well, different, and some of the other facilities in the field weren't sure what to make of that.

Perhaps the feeling that River Park was trying to be someplace special contributed to a frequent criticism of the luxury of the quarters, compared to many of the other centers and programs in the region. Jorgenson heard the talk. The snide comments found their way back to him, and he tried to work through the negativism by focusing on the people for whom treatment existed.

"I knew there was some of that negative or jealous feeling in some quarters, but, really, I just didn't have time to waste worrying about it," Jorgenson said. "We were on the go constantly. When you don't take the government money, you've made a decision to exist on private funds, and that means a lot of searching for ways to help the clients pay the cost of their treatment. We didn't want to turn anyone away because of funding, but I knew we had to be on a paying basis to keep the doors open. It was a balancing act in the early years."

A balancing act it surely was, and an often-exhausting one, both in body and mind.

If that makes it sound as though Glenn and Phyllis Jorgenson weren't enjoying their River Park experience in those early years, the impression is wrong. They were having the time of their lives.

"It's almost impossible to describe the joy I felt day after day after day," Jorgenson says as he recalls the long days, the Saturday nights spent at the center talking with clients, strolling the halls enjoying the serenity of the evening, or sitting in the coffee room listening to the clients at different stages of their recovery tell each other about changes in their thinking and their feelings.

Sometimes working with the River Park clients was almost like one never-ending piece of 12th Step work, carrying the message to alcoholics who still suffered, practicing the principles of the AA program.

Alcoholics who have been sober for some period of time and who have been active in AA and in work with other alcoholics are the first to say that the 12th Step exists for them. If it helps the one still suffering, so much the better. But it's rare to find a recovering alcoholic who won't admit he or she has said something like this after working with another: "I don't know if it did him any good, but it sure helped me with my program."

And that's how Jorgenson felt, uplifted by the opportunity to work with other alcoholics. Some days were a pure delight, even the days filled with problems and situations that needed to be resolved.

"It's hard to put into words, it was such an unusual feeling," Jorgenson says. "I'd go home at night dog-tired. I'd be wondering where the money would come from to stay open another month, praying that one or another of the clients who'd struggled that day would find a little peace through the program. At the same time, I'd be beaming. I was happier in those days than I'd been in I don't know how long."

Indeed, it is difficult for anyone who hasn't experienced the same feeling to understand the phenomenon Jorgenson describes.

Sure, each day brought a world of new problems, crises and stresses. Sure, confronting those problems and handling those crises left him tired, both physically and emotionally. And it's even true that he often worried in his quiet moments whether the things he believed in were the best things for these people of River Park.

The failures were few, but that didn't make them less painful. Once in a while, a client would leave treatment early. Jorgenson and the rest of the staff tried to talk the person into staying, finishing the last week or two weeks or whatever amount of time remained. If the person was determined to go, in spite of their urging, well, there were no doors locked at

River Park. But Jorgenson always wondered how that person fared on the outside, whether he fell back into the old ways.

Those were disappointing moments, as were the occasional reports back to the center that one or another of the clients who had "graduated" after a complete term of treatment had slipped and begun to drink again. Could we have done something different that would have given the client a better chance, Jorgenson would ask himself. Is there a gap in our program, some piece of treatment we're overlooking?

After a period of soul-searching, he'd realize again that River Park's responsibility was to give each of its clients the basic tools of recovery, based on the program of AA and administered by a staff of caring people. The outcome was best left to God. If a client didn't get the program on the first stay, it couldn't become Jorgenson's personal failure. Perhaps there was a reason, and perhaps there'd be another chance. The key was to work with each person as if he or she were the only one in the center, then leave the results to a Higher Power.

A frightening, nearly tragic incident in the early days of the program forced Jorgenson to examine everything he'd come to believe about the philosophy and the management of River Park. In the end, it affirmed those beliefs.

He received a call late one evening from the center's night supervisor. One of the clients was missing. A troubled young woman, one who had drawn much of the staff's attention during her treatment because she seemed unable to grasp the beginning steps of recovery, was nowhere to be found.

Jorgenson hurried to his car and sped the few blocks to the center. The night supervisor reported that, with the help of several clients, she had done two sweeps through the entire complex, looking in rooms, the chapel, the hallways and the garden. Glenn and Phyllis took over the search outside the building—through the trees, among the parked cars of the hospital's night shift. As they worked their way toward the riverbank, Jorgenson could feel a fear building inside him that they might not find this woman.

Eventually, they spotted her, standing rigidly on the bank, apparently working up the will to jump into the dark water. The current is light along this stretch of the river, but only a few feet from the bank the bottom drops off sharply.

Over the years, quite a story developed around this incident.

In one of the more commonly accepted tellings, Jorgenson moved toward the young woman and said softly, "I want to talk with you." The woman shook her head wildly and waded into the water. As she began to move toward the deeper part of the river, Jorgenson followed, straining against the resistance of the thigh-deep water to close the gap before the woman slipped over the drop-off. He called again, and stretched one arm toward her. The water had reached his waist, and it was nearly at the shoulders of the woman. Finally, the woman reached for his hand and allowed him to lead her back to shore.

That's the dramatic version. Jorgenson said the truth of the matter was, the woman waded into the water a short distance, and Phyllis said in a quiet but no-nonsense voice, "You come out of that water this instant."

The result was the same as in the story with the greater drama. The three ended up back at the center, where the woman was wrapped in a warm blanket. Jorgenson sat and talked with her until well past midnight, when finally she was calm enough to return to her room and fall asleep.

The incident did make Jorgenson understand that there could be no way to absolutely guarantee that such an incident would never happen again. The whole philosophy of River Park revolved around trust and respect. That meant the clients, once their initial detoxification has been completed, were to be treated as responsible human beings. They were expected to take the lead in guiding their lives on right paths. Twenty-four-hour guards and lock-downs at night would make the place a prison, not a place of hope. The clients of River Park could choose to leave. That freedom made it so much more precious each time one of them chose to stay. And the vast majority of them did choose to stay.

Believing this must be the way the center should operate, Jorgenson accepted once again that he could only do so much. He could only do what was possible, and the outcome wasn't his to decide. The results lay in the hands of a Higher Power, just as Jorgenson's own future belonged to a Higher Power, one day at a time.

Gradually, his reflections turned into prayers of gratitude to God for the successful outcome of that one night's crisis.

"Thy will be done," he whispered, and felt a sense of peace beginning to take the edges off the high emotion he'd been experiencing since the telephone rang several hours earlier.

Without the darkness, how could people appreciate the sunrise? In one form or another, that's a philosophy that dates back almost to the beginning of time.

In Jorgenson's life at River Park, it took on special meaning with incidents like the river rescue. Without crises, would he appreciate the easy successes the center experienced day after day?

Because there were successes, one after another. A few were spectacular, the stereotypical skid-row bum who straightened up, never drank again and returned to his family and his home to become a community leader and example. Many more of the successes were the quiet heroes, the men and women who had simply turned to drink and chemicals to shut out the pain of life and who found in River Park a program that let them feel the pain and handle it. How could a person, even with the daily problems and stresses, be anything but joyful when so many people were getting the help they needed?

Jorgenson felt privileged to be one of the first to welcome the good and talented and loving people who came through the doors determined to go to any lengths necessary to change their lives. These people followed the program, they worked the steps and went to the lectures and group sessions and individual appointments with counselors. They readily pitched in for the day's chores. They refilled coffee pots that always seemed to be empty, and they volunteered to sit up at night with the newcomers who struggled with both the uncertainties of a future without alcohol and the immediate pains of withdrawal.

And there were dozens of cases of severe withdrawal among the people coming into treatment, especially in the early years. River Park had no detoxification center as such, although the facilities and staff at St. Mary's Hospital were just a few corridors away. But the facilities were rarely needed as clients went through the shakes and headaches and emotional anguish of withdrawal.

Treatment-center stories of violent, dangerous cases of delirium tremens, DTs, were rife across the country as River Park was beginning its program. The uncontrollable shaking, the hallucinations and the potentially fatal seizures that marked DTs were a possibility nearly every time a new client came through the doors. But those things just didn't happen at the center. The calm approach by the staff, the helping hands of the concerned clients already on their way to recovery, the peaceful surroundings, so unlike a medical or psychiatric ward, all seemed to combine to make the withdrawal period for most clients—if not pleasant—at least relatively uneventful.

A client who'd sat up with a newcomer for a long night of hallucinations told of how the person kept telling him, "Look, you can see the little tiny nuns floating around the room. Can't you see them?" It was, the client said, a harmless enough vision and certainly one that kept him awake, as he looked for the six-inch-tall flying nuns his charge kept describing.

But of snakes and demons and dragons, the stuff of which many DT stories are made, there were none at River Park.

"I really did come to realize that it was because there was nothing to threaten our clients," Jorgenson said. "They felt safe here, and although they couldn't avoid the physical discomfort of that period of withdrawal, they generally handled it pretty routinely."

It was good that they did, because treatment began almost immediately for the new client. And one of the first challenges faced by each of the just-admitted alcoholics was stepping out in public for a meal.

As Jorgenson planned River Park's program, he was undecided whether to set up a kitchen and food service within the center itself or take the clients down the corridors to the hospital cafeteria in the connecting building. A self-contained food service would give the center undisputed control over the diet of the clients. But was that worth the expense? Especially when a hospital food service, overseen by a trained nutritionist, operated just next door?

He decided to use the hospital's cafeteria.

"As it turned out, that was an important decision," Jorgenson said. "It forced the people in treatment to have some interaction with the so-called 'normal' world, and it became one more step in the process of showing them that they weren't bad people, to be hidden away behind the walls of the convent. They were decent people with a disease that needed treatment. As decent people, they could walk into the hospital cafeteria with their heads high."

Most River Park alumni would say the trip to the cafeteria for meals was, indeed, an important step in their recovery. Most would say it became a pleasant break in their day. Most would also say that on the first morning they were told it was time to go have breakfast, they'd have done anything in the world—almost—to avoid going into a public setting.

But, as one client later joked, "You know, when we got over there and were seated at our tables eating the same scrambled eggs and drinking the same orange juice as the hospital's nurses and doctors and patients and visitors, a person coming into the cafeteria for the first time wouldn't have been able to tell who was alcoholic and who was normal. We all just looked like people who were hungry."

In fact, the story is told of the time back in 1978 when the River Park crew had just sat down for the noon meal. A man from northern South Dakota brought his tray of food to their table and joined them. The man, who knew nothing of the treatment center next door to St. Mary's, had come to the hospital to visit his wife, who'd had surgery a day earlier. Spotting an empty chair at one of the tables, the man settled in, nodded to the others at the table and prepared to pour a small cup of French dressing on the lettuce salad he'd purchased.

Remember, now, people came and went in treatment. A newcomer might join the others at any time of the day or night. Arriving at the lecture room or the chapel or the cafeteria to find an unfamiliar face or two in the chairs was common. The recovering alcoholics took the visitor for a new man and, in the best River Park tradition, tried to ease his transition into the program. Part of the mealtime experience involved spending a specific amount of time at the table.

"We were very watchful about people's eating habits," Jorgenson said. "Most alcoholics had developed atrocious diets, eating on the run if at all, spending their money on booze instead of food. We wanted to give them a sense of the place of food in the life of recovery. One of the ways we did that was to have the meals be taken in a calm, unhurried manner."

The typical meal lasted 30 minutes, and a nurse or counselor supervised the timing. Newcomers sometimes struggled just to face food. Others were in the habit of bolting down a plateful of stroganoff or spaghetti in a five-minute rampage. It didn't matter. The River Park contingent would be at the tables for 30 minutes. Clients soon learned to slow down and pace their eating, often even coming to a point where they enjoyed each mouthful and the chance to talk with other clients.

Another mealtime requirement was that a prayer be offered before anyone ate.

The visitor in our story from 1978 knew nothing of these practices. Neither did he know he'd settled among a group of recovering alcoholics. Even so, as he lifted the cup of French dressing that day, the man next to him said, "Wait, you don't start eating until the nurse prays."

Well, the visitor looked surprised, but perhaps he thought, "I guess that's all right. After all, I am in a hospital run by the Catholic nuns." Obediently, he set the dressing aside and bowed his head.

He ate rapidly after the prayer, sharing only a few words—where he was from, what he did for a living—with the others at his table. Finished with his lunch, he prepared to stand and carry his tray to the kitchen.

A River Park client placed a restraining hand lightly on his forearm.

"We all leave together," he said.

The man sat back in his seat and nodded. He folded his hands on the table in front of him and waited. Finally, everyone had finished eating and the allotted time had passed. The River Park group rose and carried their trays to the disposal area, the visitor falling in step like a veteran. As they all left the cafeteria, the River Park people turned left, heading back to the treatment center. The visitor tried to turn right, in the direction of the elevator to the surgical recovery floor and his wife's room.

A member of that 1978 River Park class remembered it this way:

"Two of our people grabbed his arms and told him this was the way we should go. At that point, the man's mild manner disappeared. He became noticeably agitated, perhaps wondering if he'd fallen in with a group of mad men and women. Just as things were growing a bit tense, the nurse who was with us approached and said, 'Who is this?' We realized our mistake, and the man scurried off down the hall, looking back over his shoulder to see if we were pursuing him."

Back in the center the clients laughed about the incident, one of them saying, "I wonder what would have happened, though, if we'd gotten him back here and he tried to tell us he didn't belong in alcohol treatment. Sure, we'd have said, each of us thought that once, too."

The cafeteria was also the site of a minor incident over menu selection that offered clients a glimpse of how convoluted and self-centered the thinking of alcoholics can become.

A client who'd been in the program about two weeks had become notorious for complaining about the food in the cafeteria. Each day, three times a day, he'd complain. It didn't matter what was on the menu, it was never what he wanted. He wanted some choice in his meals.

Staff members talked with him about using his frustration over the food selection as a way to practice some of the principles of the AA program—tolerance, patience, and willingness to pay attention to the needs of others. Still, each meal brought a complaint.

The man happened to be going through treatment in the late fall, and on November 1 the Catholic Church celebrates the Feast of All Saints as a holy day. In honor of the occasion, the hospital food service put on a feast for the noon meal. The cooks went all out, with several kinds of salad, home-baked breads, and ham and turkey and roast beef and succulent walleyed pike. The long, buffet-style meal line ended with a selection of rich pies and cakes and cookies.

As the River Park crew moved to the head of the serving line, clients poked each other in the ribs and shared raised eyebrows, waiting to see what the chronic complainer would make of this incredible feast.

He didn't disappoint them. Raising his chin and placing his hands on his hips, he looked down the long line of food and said, "Great. Look at this mess. How's a person supposed to pick something to eat when they give you this many choices?"

He may have had his troubles, but he was an important person to the other clients during those days in treatment.

"We all learned a lot about attitude, I have to say that," says one recovering alcoholic who was in the center with the complainer. "I know I started examining my behavior to see if there were places where I was just as big a complainer. Maybe God put him in my group to teach me a lesson."

River Park found countless unique ways to encourage its clients to look at their attitudes and behavior. Many of its approaches became models for other treatment programs. Sometimes, when Jorgenson saw that happening, he chuckled, especially when he recalled how the many things being copied were things that experts had told him would never work.

He became fond of quoting Father Martin, a Baltimore-area priest whose "Chalk Talk" on alcoholism and recovery became a national teaching tool because of its plain language and common-sense insights.

"Father Martin used to say in one of his films: Whatever works, works," Jorgenson said. "He just meant if something is effective, you shouldn't waste time analyzing it, you should use it."

River Park made it a point to follow that approach. Under Jorgenson's guidance, the center built a staff of people who cared, surrounded the clients with facilities that showed a respect for them as people and offered them a program of recovery—the principles of Alcoholics Anonymous—that, in a word, worked.

Jorgenson outlined a basic program of recovery from alcoholism during the early development days of River Park. He lectured frequently at that time. There were few others available to join the weekly speaking and teaching rotation, and Jorgenson's administrative and public awareness responsibilities hadn't grown as much as they did later in the center's operation.

The recovery program he suggested, preserved in an outline from one of his first lectures to clients, included:

- Having a sincere desire to stop drinking.
- Admitting and believing in our hearts that we are powerless over alcohol.
- Seeing alcoholism as a fatal and incurable illness involving body, mind and spirit.
- Considering yourselves as patients here for treatment for a fatal illness.
- Identifying alcohol as a poison, rather than a beverage, for you. Would you drink poison?
- Making it your business to understand how alcohol affects you.
- Realizing we are alcoholics.
- Learning, practicing and having faith in the 12 steps of AA.
- Believing you can arrest your illness but that you can never drink normally again.
- Using the knowledge and understanding of your illness not only to gain sobriety but also to guard against the danger of a return to drinking.
- Doing this partly by keeping in our minds a mental picture of the unmanageable life alcohol demands from us.
- Relying on God's help as the only power that can give us life.

✳ ✳ ✳

What works, works. As more and more people were discovering, River Park's approach to treatment of alcoholics worked.

Above: Glenn Jorgenson at one of his first jobs, popping popcorn at a theater in Hayti.

Right: At age 21, Jorgenson became the assistant director of South Dakota's department of old age and survivors insurance. He was appointed by South Dakota Governor Sigurd Anderson.

Below: The local newspaper editor made note of him leaving town.

THE HERALD ENTERPRISE
EDITOR: CAP NOHNER
June 10, 1948

That school was really over and that there
wouldn't be any more Hayseed column was
driven home the other morning when the editor
watched the Hayseed's conductor, Glenn Jorgenson
trudge down the road out of town shortly after
6 O'clock one morning, small suitcase in hand,
enroute to California where he will arrange to
continue his schooling. Just another young
fellow starting out in life on his own as have
thousands before him. The editor's was the last
familiar face Glenn saw as he left the old home
town. He may recall this for a long time to
come. Such trivial incidents frequently stick
a long time in a young fellow's mind until he
adjusts himself to the new work about him.

Above: Jorgenson's close friends, Jack Parr (left) and Shanard Burke (right), were the incorporators of River Park. They both served on River Park's board of directors.

Below: Joe Floyd, president of KELO Broadcasting Company, helped Jorgenson create the It's Great To Be Alive television series and also served on its board of directors.

Above: Sister Joyce Piatz, OSB, was a dietitian and Glenn Jorgenson's "right-hand-woman" at the Pierre treatment center.

Left: Dr. B. O. Lindbloom of Pierre was River Park's medical director. "He helped us for many years but never charged a dime," Jorgenson said.

Phyllis Jorgenson with daughters Julieanne (left) and Jennifer (right). The girls helped with housekeeping duties at the Pierre Center and also helped design the River Park logo (below right), which depicts words from the 23rd Psalm. Jorgenson describes the logo as "still waters and green pastures…and under God the person is the center of our efforts.

Ben Hins (below left), who was South Dakota's Director of Vocational Rehabilitation, helped the River Park founders obtain small grants for initial operating expenses. Lynn Carroll (below center), founder of the Hazelden Treatment Center in Minnesota, served as a consultant and lecturer at River Park.

Hershel Butterfield (left) was a director of the River Park Center in Pierre; Paul Rowley (right) was a director of the River Park Center in Sioux Falls.

Clarence Mortenson (left) was a West River rancher and member of the River Park Board of Directors. Tom Costello (right) was the first director of the Rapid City treatment center.

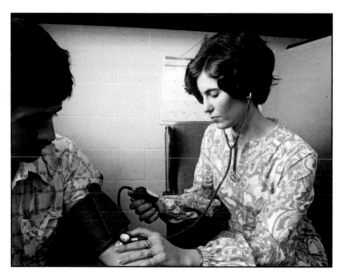

Judy Klinger, one of the directors of nursing at Pierre River Park, earned clients' praise for her compassionate care. She trained other nurses and the staff.

Father Joseph Martin (above), a nationally-known pioneer in the treatment of chemical dependency, was a guest lecturer several times at River Park.

Lloyd Jorgenson (left), Glenn's father, became one of the most popular lecturers at River Park.

The first "Family Program" staff:
Nancy Woster, Phyllis Jorgenson
and Donna Youngberg.

Don Tripp capably handled
many of the interventions with
alcoholics. The goal of the
interventions was to help the
alcoholic realize how drinking
was affecting family and work.

Mary Jordan, an interior
designer, created the
comfortable and homey décor
at River Park facilities.

Norma Neuberger, director of nursing at the Pierre treatment center, pouring coffee at the annual River Park breakfast for legislators.

Myrna Laumbach (left), Jorgenson's long-time assistant at River Park Pierre, with Kathie Pexa, who often volunteered as "overnight housemother" at the Pierre facility.

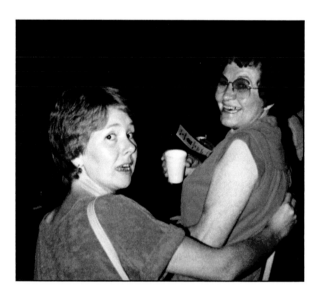

Summertime reunions at River Park's facilities in Pierre, Rapid City and Sioux Falls were always well attended, an encouraging sign that River Park programs were effective.

Loren Kampestad directed River Park's first youth awareness program at Lead-Deadwood High School.

Dennis Hellwig was the leader of River Park alumni activites, and also served on the River Park Board of Directors.

In an effort to help recovering alcoholics realize their self-worth, the staff at River Park would periodically serve a formal dinner, complete with fine linens and candlelight.

Sister Joyce and Terry Woster (at right) often led Saturday night sing-alongs for the guests.

The garden and chapel in Pierre were places of quiet reflection; however, the most popular pieces of furniture in the facility were the rocking chairs in every bedroom.

A former Catholic high school in Rapid City became River Park's second inpatient facility.

The Lindendale Motel on South Minnesota Avenue was remodeled in 1984 to create a River Park inpatient facility in Sioux Falls.

Chapter Seven

Working the Steps

One of the most gratifying discoveries in the early days of River Park's inpatient center was something Jorgenson had known in his heart but had trouble making his intellect accept until he saw it in action.

That discovery was this: The principles of Alcoholics Anonymous must be the foundation for successful recovery for most people. Jorgenson had been able to feel the truth of that when he'd started planning River Park. The principles of AA had saved his life and put him on the path of recovery. He'd experienced their power in his own life, but he'd wondered in the design stage: Could he create the program so those principles would work in a formal, group setting?

The answer, from the very first group of clients who came to River Park, was yes, a resounding yes. What works, works.

A program based on the AA principles works because it attacks the very attitudes and behaviors that prevent an alcoholic from admitting his problem and seeking help. Addiction survives in a climate of secrecy, a climate in which neither the user nor the people around him talk openly of what's happening in their lives. As the addiction grows, the secrecy deepens; feelings get pushed so deep inside the individual that they seem no longer to even exist. Nothing is real except the drinking and the secrets.

Treatment based on AA principles goes straight to the heart of that secrecy. From the beginning of the first step to the final words of the 12th, the program hits at the denial that is symptomatic of the disease. The steps invite the struggling alcoholic to abandon the fight, to admit defeat but to do so in a positive way that signals not the end of something but the beginning.

The first step says: "We admitted we were powerless over alcohol, that our lives had become unmanageable."

At River Park, the staff worked with new clients to explain the powerlessness that step described. They also concentrated on showing clients ways that life could be unmanageable even for someone who believed he was functioning productively. As the Garry Moore story made clear in a humorous way, being a debutante was no protection against alcoholism, no more than it would have been protection against chicken pox or polio or cancer.

So many people appeared at River Park's doors believing that what they had was a problem drinking, not a drinking problem. What they needed more than anything else in the world, they believed, were a few handy, practical tips on how to drink in a controlled way, not a program of recovery that suggested they not drink at all, even for one day at a time.

Internationally known tenor White Eagle, a Lakota Sioux Indian born in South Dakota, admits that when he sought treatment, what he wanted was help in controlling his drinking. He certainly didn't intend to stop drinking altogether, not at first, anyway. He had a lot of trouble admitting he was an alcoholic. Drinking had become part of his identity at an early age, and denial became his defense against the world.

White Eagle, son of a Native American minister, grew up as the only Indian pupil in an all-white school. It didn't take much pushing from classmates for the already shy youth to become convinced he wasn't as good as the other children. Alcohol became his entry into the white world, starting as early as seventh grade. He drank and belonged, he said.

"It was as a result of this glass that I belonged," White Eagle said when he talked with Glenn Jorgenson for a public awareness program. Alcohol let him and the other kids forget he was a member of a minority race. "They won't notice, and I won't notice," he said.

As he grew older, the fear of rejection continued to be a powerful force in his life. He became a marvelous singer. His slender body belied the power of the voice that rolled from his open mouth. With his fringed buckskin jackets, his deep-set dark eyes and his shoulder-length black hair swept back from his broad forehead, White Eagle cut an impressive figure on stages around the world. And when he sang, it was as if the gods had reached down and handed him the gift themselves.

But he never became comfortable with his talent, not while he still drank. And he drank long after he should have recognized the damage it was doing him, physically, emotionally and spiritually. But denial was strong.

"It will keep us from seeing the truth to the last," White Eagle said. "The drinking didn't stop, ever."

Finally, a friend forced White Eagle to see that drinking was destroying him. The singer described the confrontation on one of his albums, saying it came at a period when his voice was all but gone. He couldn't deny the truth of what his friend told him about the deteriorating condition of his voice and his life. Even so, he struggled with the first step.

"I was going to go to a recovery center to have them teach me how to control my drinking," White Eagle said.

It didn't work out that way. Once in treatment, he saw the truth of his condition and admitted he was powerless over alcohol. He described the change that admission wrought this way: "It was as if my soul had opened up and all of a sudden there was color in my life, when before there'd been only black and white."

The change began with the first step. It was only the beginning, but it was an important one.

Ralph Waite's story isn't at all like White Eagle's, except perhaps in the most important way of all—the denial of an illness.

Waite, a successful actor for many years, gained instant recognition as the wise and decent father on the popular television series *The Waltons*. But Ralph Waite couldn't hide forever from the fact that he was an alcoholic. At a crucial time in his life, he had to take the first step.

The progression of alcoholism is so gradual in many cases that it appears like normal living, Waite said.

"You don't know the trouble you're in until very late," he said. "On the surface, my life was going well…Inside, I was in deep trouble spiritually and emotionally. I was in a great deal of despair."

Waite didn't have the social or legal difficulties that bring some alcoholics to a realization that they're in trouble. He hadn't been arrested, he continued to see his children and act like a typical father, and he hadn't been fired from jobs or passed over for scripts. But he drank to get through the days.

"I knew I needed to drink in order to function," he said. "Toward the end, I was drinking all during the day in a hidden fashion."

When recovering alcoholics or family members talk about the secrets that go on in such relationships, Waite knows exactly what they mean. He says he felt dishonest about his drinking, about his life style, about his existence.

"You pretend you're feeling good, pretend life is going good, while inside you're dying," he said.

He calls alcoholism a disease of isolation and loneliness. It's a disease that feeds on itself, making it even more difficult for the alcoholic to admit there's a problem and to speak up enough to ask for help

Breaking through the denial and the isolation is the key to allowing an alcoholic to reach an acceptance of the first step. At River Park, counselors who were recovering alcoholics themselves were uniquely experienced to help in that breakthrough. They'd been there themselves, and they could see beyond the barriers and hear past the excuses and alibis.

The diversity of the clients at River Park also encouraged acceptance, Jorgenson believed. A newcomer struggling with the idea of powerlessness over alcohol often was struck by the fact that others in his group—doctors, engineers, weightlifters, computer programmers, teenagers and senior citizens—had all reached an acceptance of the first step and had openly admitted that alcohol had them beat.

"It was important at that early stage for people to know they weren't alone in this problem," Jorgenson said. "For maybe the first time in their lives, at least since they started abusing alcohol or other drugs, they weren't around people from whom they had to keep secrets. And once they saw all these other people talking without shame or embarrassment about being powerless, they were able to take that step themselves."

Quite often, the second half of that first step—our lives had become unmanageable—posed an even bigger obstacle to recovery than did the idea of powerlessness over alcohol.

Many alcoholics, whether they'd admit it to anyone else in the entire world or not, knew in their hearts that their drinking wasn't normal. They may have had all the excuses in the world—the wife didn't understand them, the boss was a slave driver, the money didn't stretch far enough, the world was impossible. When the liquor's effects wore off, though, they lay in a pit of isolation and knew they were not drinking like other people.

They'd done it all too many times to hide from themselves. They'd gone into too many bars intending to have but a single drink, two beers at the most. They'd staggered out at closing time shaky and inebriated. They'd missed too many school plays and concerts by losing track of time during "happy hour" down at the corner tavern. They knew that alcohol had them overpowered.

Somehow, though, it was a big step from that admission to an understanding that their lives were out of control. They were managing, weren't they? And against some pretty heavy odds, too, the kinds of problems that would bring a lesser person to his knees.

Well, at River Park, that's what the program tried to do, figuratively, at least: bring the individual to his knees. But it had to be done in such a way that it was the client's decision to take the first step. It couldn't be forced. It could be encouraged, though, and there was a big difference in the two approaches. It was a difference that other treatment centers sometimes couldn't understand and that some traditional AA members couldn't appreciate.

River Park didn't use the hard confrontation that some treatment programs used. That was one of Jorgenson's early decisions, and it was one he never considered changing, not once.

Earlier he talked about his belief that if people are treated as they could be, they will become what they could be. That philosophy permeated the treatment program. Clients were treated with respect, with concern and with love.

Jorgenson became fond of quoting a story about Dr. Karl Menninger, who once said the program of treatment at his hospital was love. If that didn't work, he said, "We double the dose." River Park's treatment program started out with a double dose of love.

During River Park's infancy, some treatment centers in other parts of the country were gaining reputations for putting alcoholics on the road to recovery with programs of harsh confrontation. They believed an alcoholic could only be treated successfully if his spirit was first broken. The person needed to be torn down and rebuilt, they said.

To do that, some centers forced newcomers to strip naked and lie on the floor while counselors and other clients heaped verbal abuse on them, calling them names, cursing them, ridiculing them. Other programs used harsh punishments aimed at degrading the individual and taking away his self-respect. The client was made to believe he was nothing, so that he could be rebuilt in a sober fashion. That was the theory behind such approaches, at least.

Jorgenson refused to believe such methods would ultimately be successful.

"You don't have to tell an alcoholic he's worthless," Jorgenson said. "That's exactly what he's been telling himself for longer than you can imagine. The people who came to River Park didn't need to be broken; they needed to be lifted up and made whole."

The counselors Jorgenson hired, as well as the nurses and other staff members, became skilled at what might be considered soft confrontation. Clients weren't allowed to avoid looking at the consequences of their drinking or drug use. Those who denied they'd been "that bad" were given every opportunity to consider how their alcoholism had affected career, family, friendships and relationship with God. The technique that developed at River Park became incredibly effective, without ever once having a staff member "come down on" a client in an abusive, degrading way.

What the counselors did was to patiently but persistently work with the client, moving toward a realization of what had happened in that person's life. The client who denied his life had become unmanageable, for example, would be given opportunities to examine the signs that perhaps he'd been more out of control than he believed. Jail, divorce, dismissal from work, reprimands, all could be examples of a life that was unmanageable.

So could more subtle shortcomings.

The client who promised a 10-year-old daughter he'd be in the audience for her ballet recital might have gone home late that night and told the family he'd been held up at the office. In conversations with River Park counselors, he might come to admit he'd been so late because he'd come back from a three-hour, three-or-four martini lunch to face a stack of contracts that needed to be completed before morning and that could have been done if he hadn't included liquor in his lunch order.

If that kind of thing happened again and again, the client might have written each one off as a separate bit of bad luck. He could blame the boss or the wife or the police or the accident on the freeway or the flat tire, but if he really was an alcoholic, at some point he had to blame the drinking and the behavior it produced.

In Alcoholics Anonymous, people who come to accept the truth of the first step often are said to have surrendered. They'd been fighting so long against the idea that they couldn't control their drinking that it came as something of a relief when they quit fighting.

River Park's approach was like that. It gave the client an opportunity to say, "I've had enough. I don't want to fight any longer. I surrender." To Jorgenson's way of thinking, voluntary surrender by an alcoholic was a positive decision. Forced submission of the kind practiced in some hard confrontation programs was a negative decision.

Negative decisions don't work well in dealing with alcoholics. An alcoholic who is forced to take the first step is much more likely to go back on his decision at some point in the future than is the alcoholic who is given the opportunity to surrender to the program. A forced decision leaves within the person the seed for a future rationalization that "I really didn't mean it. They were just pushing so hard." That isn't the attitude River Park wanted to instill in its clients.

"I believe surrender is basic to solving the problems of the alcoholic," Jorgenson said. "Surrender comes from within, and it opens the whole person to the possibility of recovery."

✳ ✳ ✳

Surrender to the first step of the program opened the alcoholic to the next step: "Came to believe a Power greater than ourselves could restore us to sanity."

Once an alcoholic accepted the fact of his or her own powerlessness, it was a small step to accepting the possibility that some greater Power could help restore some semblance of control to life. It was a small step, but not an easy one. Even in River Park's setting, some clients struggled with this step and with the third: "Made a decision to turn our will and our lives over to the care of God as we understood him."

These two steps sounded a lot like religion, and alcoholics sometimes seem to have a pretty skewed view of God and religion.

At River Park, clients were urged to keep an open mind on the topic. They were asked to set aside their past problems with religion or with God and to merely be receptive to two ideas: First, that there might be a Power greater than themselves, and second, that if there were such a Power, it could do things for them that they couldn't do for themselves. Given those possibilities, didn't it make sense to at least be willing to turn their lives over to that kind of Power?

The gentle approach, in which counselors and other staff talked of a spiritual awakening, rather than a religious experience, seemed to work in even some of the most hardened cases.

"We were warned early in the program that we couldn't push the spiritual aspect of recovery or we'd lose a lot of people right away in treatment," Jorgenson said. "I didn't ever see how you could run a program of recovery without stressing the spiritual side. It's such an integral part of the whole concept."

So the River Park program included frequent discussions of Higher Power, prayer and meditation, all part of the spiritual healing process. And most clients quickly embraced that part of their recovery.

"Perhaps it was because the River Park staff members, recovering alcoholics themselves, could honestly say, "We're not telling you that you must do this. We're only saying that we tried everything else, and nothing else worked. This approach worked for us, and it's worked for a lot of people who came through the doors here before you did."

Once again, what works, works.

"It was very effective, coming from people who'd been there," Jorgenson said. "At some point in each treatment cycle, the counselors would tell their own stories of alcoholism and recovery, and the clients would understand that they were working with people who had done what they'd done, tried what they'd tried, failed often and finally found a way to stay sober."

Staff members often shared their own initial skepticism about the spiritual approach to recovery, and told of how it had seemed to work for them even while they were still uncertain if they were ready to give in to it.

"That's a powerful message for a struggling alcoholic, and it seemed to hit home," Jorgenson said.

Each morning at River Park began with a visit to the chapel in St. Mary's hospital. Alone as a group of recovering alcoholics, the clients would sit in the quiet chapel and take stock of their day, listening to readings from the book *24 Hours A Day*, meditating and praying or simply sitting silently. While some clients expressed surprise and even displeasure at the prospect of beginning the day in a chapel, most soon came to look forward to that quiet time as a chance to ask for strength in the coming day and to give thanks for the past 24 hours.

"Not only that, but we'd find that clients often went to the chapel during free periods throughout the day," Jorgenson said. "It wasn't unusual for me to stop in for a brief moment of prayer and find one or two clients sitting in the pews with tears on their cheeks and eyes cast toward heaven. Those moments are some I'll treasure from those days at River Park."

Opening up spiritually was important to a client's recovery, but so was accepting responsibility and so was learning to enjoy life.

Responsibility came through the daily chores clients shared. They did some of the cleaning and vacuuming. They made coffee and orange juice. They mopped up spills in the day room and emptied the wastebaskets and garbage cans throughout the center. Dividing up the chores was one way to keep the costs of additional staff down a bit in the early days. But Jorgenson said if he'd had unlimited access to funds he'd still have had the clients do chores.

"It taught them about responsibility, these people whose lives had been so undisciplined for so long," Jorgenson said. "That may sound simple, but it worked. So did the regular hour for rising, the scheduled meal times, and the evening quiet time and lights out. All of those things brought discipline to these lives."

Saturday-night sing-alongs helped show recovering alcoholics they could enjoy themselves without liquor.

The sing-alongs started as a break in the week's routine, a chance for clients to let off some steam by joining Sister Joyce and a varied collection of other guitar players in an old-fashioned songfest. The first hour of the sing-along was required for all clients. After that, they could go back to their rooms or watch TV or work on their programs. Many chose to remain and sing well into the evening.

"My experience with Saturday nights and singing had always involved being drunk enough not to care that I was making a fool of myself," one sing-along regular said. "River Park's sing-alongs taught me that I could have as much fun or more without liquor. I was never a great singer, but at River Park, nobody seemed to mind, because we were just being ourselves and enjoying life."

Being themselves and enjoying life.

Those were key parts of the River Park prescription for recovery. But so was hard work. Not the work that went with the daily chores. That was child's play compared to the work River Park clients were expected to do if they wished to get the most out of their time in treatment.

✳ ✳ ✳

The real work in the program involved the steps, and those who'd struggled with steps Two and Three discovered that much more was expected of them in steps Four and Five.

Step Four of the AA program says alcoholics: "Made a searching and fearless moral inventory of ourselves." Step Five carries that into action, saying they: "Admitted to God, to ourselves, and to another human being the exact nature of our wrongs."

This was the process some recovering alcoholics called clearing out the dead wood. It was one more way to brush away the secrecy and the denial that had kept the downward spiral of alcoholism from being arrested sooner.

With the first week of treatment, clients began to review their lives, taking that searching and fearless moral inventory the steps suggested were critical to recovery. The inventory was an arduous task for most clients. They were dredging up long-buried resentments, old wounds from as far back as childhood. They were examining mistakes they'd made, wrongs they'd done, lies they'd told, people they'd hurt, crimes they'd committed. It took all the courage these still shaky alcoholics had to stay with the inventories and to do the fearless searching the step required of them.

But as the River Park staff stressed, an inventory is about both the liabilities and the assets. A business that fails to count its assets with its liabilities doesn't have a true picture of its condition. The same was true for a recovering alcoholic. Clients were urged to look at their strengths as well as their weaknesses, to count their positive attributes along with the negatives.

And when the list was finished, usually on paper and often covering several sheets of a notebook, the client shared the inventory with God and with another person as directed in Step Five.

At River Park, fifth steps were taken with one of several carefully chosen members of the area clergy. These were people whose training and life's work had put them often on the receiving end of confessions of one kind or another. It took only a modest amount of training for Jorgenson and his staff to understand what was necessary to help the fifth-steppers. And what was necessary more than anything else was that they would be patient, attentive and non-judgmental listeners as the clients unburdened themselves of everything that had bothered them in their lives.

These fifth steps often took several hours as the recovering alcoholic shared with another human being events and behaviors and feelings he hadn't told anyone before, not ever. It was one more way to break down the wall of silence and secrecy that lets alcoholism survive.

At the conclusion of their fifth steps, many clients emerged almost as if in a trance. For most, it was the first time they'd taken stock of their lives without blaming someone else. It was the first time they'd said to another person, after admitting it to themselves, "This is where I've failed to be what I could be. This is where I didn't behave as I know I should have." And, having identified their wrongdoing and their shortcomings and having accepted responsibility for them, the clients then left those things behind when they walked from the room.

Sister Joyce used to refer to the trance-like state of the post-fifth-step client as "that walking on clouds feeling." Indeed, many seemed to be doing just that. They emerged from the fifth step process lighter, happier, as if a load had been set down after having been shouldered for far too long.

The clients were encouraged to take some personal time after their fifth steps. They walked in the park, sat on the patio, meditated in the chapel, simply experiencing the feeling of being whole. It was the climactic moment in most treatment experiences, and Jorgenson couldn't imagine a successful program that stopped short of this step in recovery.

"It was so important to long-term sobriety for the alcoholic to get through the fifth step and feel the freedom and release of having opened himself up to God and to another person," Jorgenson said. "Once that process had been completed, the clients were very near the end of their stay with River Park. There'd be a lot more work for them to do, a lifetime of recovery. But I was convinced that if they'd completed a thorough fourth and fifth steps, and if they made the connections with AA after they left treatment, they were well on the road to a successful sobriety."

In the days that remained before their treatment ended, clients who'd finished their fifth steps worked on the remaining steps of the program.

Step Six: "Were entirely ready to have God remove all these defects of character" flowed naturally from the inventory written in Step Four and shared in Step Five. Step Seven: "Humbly asked him to remove our shortcomings," became part of a daily program of recovery, as did Step Ten:

"Continued to take personal inventory and when we were wrong promptly admitted it."

Step Eight, "Made a list of all persons we had harmed and became willing to make amends to them all," could be started in treatment, but its companion Step Nine, "Made direct amends to such people wherever possible, except when to do so would injure them or another," required that the recovering alcoholic make contact directly with many people who could only be reached after the client left River Park.

The other steps in the program are Eleven, "Sought through prayer and meditation to improve our conscious contact with God as we understood Him, praying only for knowledge of His will for us and the power to carry that out," and Twelve, "Having had a spiritual awakening as a result of these steps, we tried to carry this message to alcoholics and to practice these principles in all our affairs."

Both steps were such that clients could begin to practice them while they were in River Park. Prayer and meditation were integral parts of the treatment program, while carrying the message and practicing principles of honest, open behavior were what sobriety would, or should, be all about.

The design of River Park's treatment program encouraged clients to act in ways consistent with the twelve steps. The more familiar the recovering alcoholic became with every part of the program while he was in treatment, the better were his chances of maintaining a healthy and happy sobriety after he left River Park.

"Many of our clients had to handle real fear as the day approached for them to go home," Jorgenson said. "They wanted to live sober and they knew they could do it in River Park. They worried that when they went home, the old habits and actions would take over. I always considered that a somewhat healthy fear. It showed they weren't overconfident."

At the same time, he suffered with those unsure clients as they prepared to step back into the world that had so confounded them just a month earlier. They had round-the-clock support in River Park. Would they remember to seek the same support from AA members when they got back home? Most did, it turned out. Most stayed sober, too.

To improve the odds even more, Jorgenson began to set up an after-care program, so that clients would have not only Alcoholics Anonymous to support them after treatment but also a support group sponsored by River Park.

"It just seemed clear to me that we had some responsibility to continue to participate in the recovery of the people we sent back to the communities," Jorgenson said. "We'd taken them in, given them a set of tools that worked, but we needed to follow up with them, too."

Chapter Eight

Going Public

Glenn Jorgenson worked long days to get River Park started, and he worked even longer days to keep it running. So much had to be done, so many things had to be learned and, as he realized rather quickly, few successful models existed—models for the kind of treatment center he knew could help people.

It was difficult, demanding work, but the rewards came every day. He felt rewarded each time a man or woman who'd come to the center as a desperate alcoholic walked out to take up a full life. So much gratitude flowed from each of these beginning-to-heal people, and so much promise.

With his wife Phyllis and with his father Lloyd always ready to handle one more task, with a growing staff of recovering alcoholics quickly learning the River Park way of treating the clients, each day offered a new chance to help others.

Yet Jorgenson knew there was so much more to be done.

His work in the state personnel agency and his research and reading while drawing up the plans for River Park had convinced him that alcoholism was a major national problem.

But that was nothing compared to what he was learning every day as he walked the halls of River Park and talked with the clients. The more the beds filled and the more the lecture room and chapel overflowed, the more he realized the program had only begun to peel back the top layer of the chemical dependency problem. Across South Dakota and across the nation, thousands upon thousands of alcoholics still suffered, thousands upon thousands of households still lived the endless hell that had been his own life before sobriety.

How to make people understand that it didn't have to be that way? How to get the message out?

Inpatient treatment was working, one alcoholic at a time. Alcoholics were finding the road to recovery—five or six or seven each week, 25 or 30 each month. Considering that those were people who might otherwise never have begun to recover, that was an amazing statistic. But it wasn't enough. There had to be a way to reach beyond that, Jorgenson thought. So many more people were suffering.

Each day the evening newspaper's public record section carried half a dozen names of people sentenced to jail time or fines for driving while intoxicated. Others were listed for public intoxication and still others had been convicted of other crimes—assault, disturbing the peace, domestic violence—that likely resulted from situations in which alcohol played a role. Surely there must be a way to reach some of those people with the news of River Park's successful program.

The center had handled some terrible cases—men caught driving after drinking for the fourth or fifth time, men and women behind the wheels of cars when their blood-alcohol content was two and three times the legal limit for operating a motor vehicle. The center had accepted people who'd boozed themselves out of everything they held dear, men and women who showed up at the door with little more than the clothes on their backs. It had sent them back to the world with hope and a fresh start.

Other people—alcoholics, families of alcoholics, professional men and women whose counseling or medical or legal businesses brought them into contact with alcoholics, employers—needed to know things could change.

And yet, Jorgenson understood the immense challenge he faced to carry that message to the public. It was one thing to talk sobriety and treatment with an alcoholic who had completely lost hope. It would be quite another thing to take the same message to people who didn't see what their drinking was doing to them and their families, or to people who didn't understand chemical dependency at all. The numbers of such folks were legion, and many of them had neither desire nor time to listen to talk about alcoholism.

Let's face it, Jorgenson said to himself more than once as he wrestled with the problem. The subject matter simply makes people uncomfortable. They don't know much about it, and what they do know is stereotype, half-truth at best, perceptions formed from gossip and street talk.

The truth was, in the early days of River Park, if a person showed an interest in the subject, his friends or family might think he had a problem. How would that affect his public image?

How many times had Jorgenson talked with people who looked desperate for help but who told him, "Listen, I'm not asking for me, you understand, but I have this buddy who sometimes lets his drinking get out of hand a little bit." Sometimes, as the conversation continued, it turned out there was, indeed, a friend with a drinking problem. As often as not, though, the person with the problem was sitting across the table from Jorgenson and trying mightily to appear in control.

Jorgenson recognized that he was fighting not only the denial of the disease itself but also the public stigma that surrounded the world of chemical dependency. Most people in the country accepted liquor but rejected alcoholism as a disease. Wasn't it perfectly all right for a man to be a two-fisted drinker and a party animal? Sure, there might be some fights, a scraped fender, hurt feelings at home, but that was pretty normal. From his early days in Hayti and his political travels across South Dakota, Jorgenson knew that a guy who really knew how to hold his liquor was a respected member of society. A person needed to be able to drink these days, and a person of breeding knew how to control the drinking. That was accepted.

But an acknowledged alcoholic? A man or a woman who came out and admitted he or she had lost the power to control the drinking? A drunk trying to quit, to change?

That was something many people shied away from.

It was just that social stigma, that public attitude that drinking is okay but being an uncontrolled drinker was not, that was keeping a lot of suffering people from seeking treatment, too. In the short while that River Park had been open, Jorgenson had lost count of the number of times he'd been with men and women who admitted, yes, maybe they had a problem with the booze, but how could they go to treatment? They'd lose their job. They'd lose their friends. They'd lose their standing in the community.

This was the early 1970s, after all. Alcoholics Anonymous chapters operated in many of the larger communities of the country, and there'd been a few stories in the newspapers and magazines about that program and how it was helping people. But it was far from an enlightened time. The image of the alcoholic as a skid-row bum with three days' growth of beard and a bottle of cheap wine wrapped in a brown paper bag was almost universally accepted.

Right in Pierre, the home of River Park, stories were told of townspeople who drove past the AA club about the time of the evening meetings, just to catch a glimpse of the folks who were going to that place. Some of the old-timers in the club laughed that off, but they had to admit that the notion of having people stare at the clubhouse door was one more barrier for newcomers, already reluctant and uncertain.

The attitude had to change if alcoholics were going to get the treatment that was available, Jorgenson knew. Somehow, the perception of the scratch-bum had to be erased from people's minds and replaced with a more accurate picture of the typical alcoholic.

And as Jorgenson knew, there was no typical alcoholic. River Park had already worked with retired mail carriers in their 70s, as well as with fresh-faced teen-aged girls not yet out of high school. The alcoholic who sought treatment in River Park might be, indeed *had* been, a lawyer, a doctor, a housewife, and a day laborer.

Each of those recovering River Park alumni carried the message to their home communities, Jorgenson knew. Referrals to the center picked up in towns and cities where River Park alumni lived. People saw the change that had taken place in that person's life, and they came to believe it could happen to them, too. If it were possible to have a recovering alcoholic prompt others to seek help simply by walking sober through the streets of his hometown, it certainly should be possible to tell that story in other communities.

That would require visible programs aimed at educating the public to the fact that alcoholism is a disease that can be treated. It would require programs aimed at raising the public awareness to the tremendous prevalence of alcoholism, to the signs that someone has a drinking problem and to the opportunities for treatment available at River Park and other treatment centers.

The obvious answer was for Jorgenson himself to carry the River Park message. He designed the program; he directed the operations of the center each day. He knew better than anyone else what was intended in the treatment program.

But how would such a message be most effectively carried? For public awareness to work, River Park needed to be more than a building, more than a converted convent on the shores of the Missouri River. It needed to have a personality, something to make people care about it the first time they heard of it.

Jorgenson's most faithful confidantes and backers, including Shanard Burke, suggested that the way to get people to care would be for Jorgenson to be the public figure identified with the center and its programs.

"You have the ability to talk in public, Glenn," his friend said. "You're good at it. It seems so natural, and people respond to you. I wouldn't be any good at that sort of thing. None of us would. In fact, I can't think of anyone else involved in alcohol treatment at any level who is so ideally suited for the task."

The argument made sense, Jorgenson had to admit. He'd gained some confidence in public speaking through his political and state government years. He was no stranger to a microphone or podium. And he surely did care deeply about the message he hoped to carry.

But wouldn't he run the risk of offending people, too? One of the traditions of Alcoholics Anonymous, the 11th, says, "Our public relations policy is based on attraction rather than promotion. We need always maintain personal anonymity at the level of press, radio and television." For some of the old-timers in the clubs, a strict interpretation of that meant no recovering alcoholic should ever speak publicly about the subject.

And yet, River Park wasn't Alcoholics Anonymous. Yes, it had been founded on the principles of AA. One of its basic messages to recovering alcoholics had been that an alcoholic's chances of staying sober and living a joyful life increased dramatically if he or she became a regular at AA. So how could it be wrong if a recovering alcoholic simply acknowledged the fact that he'd had a drinking problem and had found the beginnings of sobriety at River Park? And how could that message be carried without at least acknowledging that the program was based on the principles of Alcoholics Anonymous?

Jorgenson struggled with the issue, seeing the opportunity to spread a good message, worrying that those who believed he was taking a wrong approach might turn their criticism on River Park itself. Nothing must be done that would harm the center and its programs, he told himself.

As he wrestled with the problem, during long days of meditation in the River Park chapel and atop the river bluff in his still-favorite lookout point, Jorgenson gradually crystallized a guiding philosophy in a few simple statements that had been subconsciously building ever since his awakening in his own treatment program. His most fervent prayer remained each day that God's will be done. But how to be sure that a decision was indeed God's will, not just his own desire?

The dilemma was exactly the same as that posed by the third phrase of the Serenity Prayer: "The wisdom to know the difference." Ah, wouldn't it be much easier to have the serenity to accept things that can't be changed and courage to change things that can be changed if people only knew for sure which was which? As Jorgenson prayed the Serenity Prayer time after time, he now prayed many times a day for God's will to be made clear in the matter of public programs for River Park.

When it came, the answer wasn't as dramatic as his roadside message to build the center, but it became the foundation for all the decisions he would make during the rest of his life's work with River Park. The test of any action or decision, he decided, could be found in three simple questions:

- Does the proposed action or decision glorify God?
- Is this action, program or decision needed?
- Is anyone else performing the same function or offering the same program?

Anything River Park did in the future would have to meet each of those standards, Jorgenson decided. If a proposed action didn't glorify God, it must not be worth doing. If it did, then the path was clear. The question of need should follow the first answer almost as night follows the day, he believed. And if an action were for the glory of God and were needed, and if no one else was taking care of the problem, how could it be wrong to go ahead as enthusiastically as possible?

Jorgenson applied those standards to the idea of moving into a program of public awareness and education. Done for the purpose of helping suffering alcoholics, a program of carrying the River Park message could only glorify God, he believed. The need he saw every day—in the letters and phone calls from relatives of alcoholics, in the court news, in the highway deaths and jail sentences and wasted lives. And his review of the literature of alcoholism combined with his daily experiences in running River Park convinced him that no one anywhere in the country was making a concerted effort to expand understanding of the disease, its symptoms and its treatment.

So he plunged ahead, seeking opportunities to tell the River Park story in any forum that would accept him. He contacted service clubs, church groups, medical meetings and other public gatherings that offered the opportunity to talk about alcoholism and treatment. He began to stop at radio and television stations as he traveled, and to visit the local newspapers, daily and weekly, in the communities he visited.

He advertised on the radio, not with screaming words and dark images of downtrodden drunks and bums but with a gentle message of caring and hope, a message designed specifically to convey the unique River Park approach to treatment. He talked with legislators throughout each session held in Pierre during the winter months.

He even began having the center host the entire Legislature for a breakfast at River Park. It gave busy lawmakers a glimpse of the facilities and the program. If they came just for the scrambled eggs and the orange juice, well, they got it. If they carried away a little better understanding of what alcoholism was all about, so much the better.

The River Park breakfast became one of the highlights of session for many legislators. Jorgenson and his staff rarely asked the senators and representatives anything more serious than, "Would you like me to warm up that coffee?" The atmosphere, the menu and the lack of lobbying for specific legislation were all in sharp contrast to the almost nightly banquets hosted by statewide interest groups. In those events, the pre-dinner cocktails flowed freely, the steaks and shrimp and wine were plentiful.

"You leave most of these dinners and you feel lousy, stuffed, half-drunk and just ready to go home for the night," one legislator told Jorgenson. "I leave your breakfast uplifted and ready to put in a good day's work."

All of these contacts—the legislators, the public audiences, the newspaper and radio reporters—convinced Jorgenson that when people were able to listen to the message, they got it. It just took so many contacts to carry that message each day. And each contact still seemed to involve a fight to break through the stereotypes and the stigmas.

That was borne out the evening River Park hosted a public meeting of its own on the possibilities of treatment. Jorgenson had rented a meeting room in a Pierre motel. He'd advertised the meeting, lined up a guest speaker and carried in a supply of strong coffee, juice and cookies. He got there early that evening, accompanied by Phyllis. Jack Parr and Shanard Burke showed up a few minutes after the Jorgensons, as did Dr. B. O. Lindbloom, who'd added the role as River Park's medical officer to his long-established family practice in Pierre.

The small group eagerly arranged the chairs, spread the cookies in eye-pleasing fashion on the plates and waited for the public to arrive. The group waited and waited. At the scheduled hour for the start of the program, they waited still, the only ones in the room.

Jorgenson was crushed. His friend Shanard joked, "You know, the art of a good public meeting organizer is to always have the room be a little smaller than the crowd, Glenn." He patted Jorgenson on the arm as he said it, but it was plain that he was disappointed, too.

Phyllis, although she'd had high hopes for a good turnout, was more philosophical about the failed evening.

"You really can't expect a lot of people to just walk right in to a meeting advertised as being about alcoholism," she told Glenn. "Look at how long you were unable to face the truth. Look at all the people who we get at the center and how hard some of them have tried to avoid looking at this problem. People feel threatened by the idea of a public meeting. What might their friends think? What if a boss saw them? Somehow, there's a way to make it less threatening and still get the message out. Someday, I just feel it, you'll be able to fill rooms like this to overflowing with people eager to learn more about this disease."

Someday, but what about now, Jorgenson thought to himself. Patience, he counseled. It takes time. Look how much success we've had. All that's needed is to keep working and keep praying for direction.

Slowly the direction showed itself. During a trip from Sioux Falls to Pierre, Jorgenson stopped at the local radio station, KORN, in Mitchell. A popular central South Dakota station in the city that billed itself as the home of the world's only Corn Palace, KORN had been a target of Jorgenson's visits a couple of previous times. This time, something entirely unexpected happened.

"I sat in the office with the station's day manager, talking about alcoholism, describing River Park's program and some of its early successes, and stressing quite a bit the need for more public awareness of the disease," Jorgenson said. "All of a sudden the guy jumped to his feet and said, 'C'mon! I'm going to put you on the air live,' he said. 'We can tell a little of that story right here. I'm going to interview you.'"

Jorgenson recalls asking for a moment to visit the restroom.

"I stood in there just about in a panic for a moment," he says. "I remember leaning against the tile wall, asking over and over, 'Oh, God, what do I do now?'"

What he did was pray for guidance. The Third Step Prayer (God, I offer myself to Thee, to build with me and to do with me as Thou wilt…) seemed to bring a sense of purpose and peace as he realized that he had only to rely on God's will. What the interview might mean, he didn't know, but he felt comfortable in the assurance that he would only try as best he could to get the message out.

"I hardly remember what we talked about in specific ways," Jorgenson said later. "It seemed to go a lot faster than I thought it would, and I was surprised when the guy hit a couple of switches and said we were finished."

Really, it was just the beginning.

The station manager thanked Jorgenson for taking the time to sit for an interview, then said, "You know, you ought to do a series of shows on this topic. You handle it well, and you could really reach a lot of people with broadcasts."

As he left the station and continued his drive home to Pierre, Jorgenson chuckled at the manager's suggestion. A series of broadcasts, indeed. Who would tune in to a scheduled program on alcoholism? Just an overly enthusiastic radio guy tossing off a crazy notion.

And yet, he'd just done a live interview during a pretty prime time of the day for a respected radio station. The manager didn't seem like a flake. He obviously thought his listeners would keep their dials set on KORN. The guy wouldn't waste his time on the interview if he thought it would lose his audience.

The more Jorgenson thought about it, the more potential he saw in the idea of a series of broadcasts. Just think. If a person could find a way to broadcast the message of River Park, wouldn't that be a non-threatening way to present it? A person who feared he had a drinking problem, a wife or husband or child or parent who wondered if the problem existed in the family, they wouldn't have to leave the house and go to a public meeting. They could sit by the radio right in their own home and perhaps learn enough to encourage them to make that first step toward help.

Jorgenson began to consider ways to make such a program successful. He didn't know it then, but the answer lay just ahead. It required only a good deal of prayer, the willingness on Jorgenson's part to take a risk—a leap of faith, so to speak—and a couple of helping hands. The help came from a nationally known television minister and from a Sioux Falls broadcast executive, a man Jorgenson had known many, many years earlier as a teen-ager working in the big city for the summer.

Chapter Nine

It's Great To Be Alive

Jorgenson may not have been able to spread River Park's message as far and as fast as he wanted to, but both he and the treatment center's approach were beginning to catch the eyes of people who would become important to future growth and success.

One such person was Robert Schuller.

Schuller was a well-spoken, energetic minister of the Gospel whose name and voice were recognized by religious folks from one end of the country to the other. His broadcast *Hour of Power* was a popular radio program, and his televised services from the Crystal Cathedral in southern California drew millions of viewers.

He was a man who understood the power of the broadcast message, and when he and Jorgenson became acquainted, he stressed the advantages of seeking the widest possible audience for the message that River Park was trying to convey. He rarely expressed a pessimistic sentiment. His own message tended to be upbeat, and that positive attitude was contagious, something Jorgenson had been trying to put into his own life from the day he left treatment.

"Bob Schuller really helped me find a willingness to dream big things as I pondered how to further public awareness," Jorgenson said. "He was tremendously successful in his life's work, and he refused to think others wouldn't be, too."

Pumped up once more, Jorgenson continued his public rounds. He began to work more on what the broadcasters call PSAs, public service announcements. He was finding, as more and more River Park alumni showed up in towns across the region with a new spring in their step and a fresh purpose to their life, that his reception in the newsrooms of newspapers and broadcast stations was becoming increasingly cordial.

Most editors were willing to update the River Park story on a regular basis, and to print or broadcast notices of events. But the ground-floor story of alcoholism still was barely being told. The stereotypes hung on, built by decades of misunderstanding. Sadly, just as stubborn and just as hard to erase was the reluctance of people to talk openly about the disease and its impact on their lives or the lives of their families.

To break down the walls that prevented the public from talking about alcoholism the same way they did about diabetes or cancer or heart disease was the task Jorgenson faced. As he pressed on in the effort, he made a powerful ally. As it turned out, the man had given Jorgenson a helping hand many decades earlier. The help he'd offer now would be a key to the success of River Park's public awareness program.

The man was Joe Floyd. He'd hired a teen-aged Glenn Jorgenson to work at his movie theater in downtown Sioux Falls many summers ago. Now, he owned a broadcasting company that operated KELO-TV. KELO's signal reached far into Minnesota, Iowa and Nebraska, and the station's on-air personalities became among the region's best-known celebrities.

Floyd and station manager Evans Nord had always been receptive to River Park's public-service announcements, giving them multiple plays in prime time spots.

With Floyd's encouragement, Nord and Jorgenson would get together from time to time and kick around ways to create a program on alcoholism. It had to be something that would break down the barriers of ignorance. It had to be something educational, to help people understand what a terrible disease alcoholism was and how many people it affected. It had to be something that would draw and hold the attention of viewers, something with "prime-time" appeal.

Most of all, Jorgenson kept saying during the brainstorming sessions, it had to be something rooted firmly in hope. It couldn't be a program that just laid out all the bad things that can happen with alcoholism, although that subject shouldn't be avoided. But to make people want to seek help, the program must give them hope that things could get better.

As Jorgenson well knew, the world of alcoholism is a bottomless pit. Every day can seem worse than the one before it, and rarely does an active alcoholic feel any hope that life can be different. In the alcoholic's life, if things are going to change, they'll change for the worse. It never occurs to an alcoholic that it's going to get any better.

Jorgenson promised himself that, no matter what else he was able to do in this still-unplanned program of his, he was going to have a strong dose of hope. It was going to reflect a little catch phrase of a greeting he found himself using over and over in his sobriety.

"Morning, Glenn," someone would say as they met on the street. "How are things going with you?"

With a hearty nod of his head and a big smile, Jorgenson would reply, "Best day of my life."

That approach to the new day was a key to Jorgenson's choice for a motto at River Park. Early in the process, he'd settled on these words: "It's Great To Be Alive." That would be the attitude that must come through clearly in any program about alcoholism that Jorgenson would produce.

At KELO, Floyd and Nord promised Jorgenson they'd help in any way they could, with production, filming, editing and promotion. But what would the program be?

The answer came in the mail.

Jorgenson sat one day at his office next door to the coffee room in River Park. He sorted through the pile of mail that had accumulated while he was on the latest swing through the state. Much of it was bills, what else? They had to be paid, and the money would be found, somehow. But the center also attracted a considerable amount of professional mail, notices of seminars on alcoholism and workshops for counselors and on and on.

This day, the mail carried an advertisement for Freedom Fest. The event would be a huge convention of Alcoholics Anonymous, with recovering addicts from all over the world expected to attend. A host of movie stars, celebrities, and national personalities were to be part of the program. And it was in Minneapolis.

Minneapolis was a city Jorgenson knew well. A progressive, energetic community, Minneapolis—along with its sister-city, St. Paul—was fast becoming one of the best run and most enjoyable of the nation's big cities. It was most of a day's drive from River Park in Pierre, but that wasn't what Jorgenson was thinking as he stared at the flyer advertising Freedom Fest.

He was thinking of the celebrities and what an impact they'd have at the gathering.

If a movie star or a U.S. senator or a big-league baseball player could be an alcoholic, that knowledge could break through a lot of denial in the rest of the population.

If a celebrity could stand up in public and say he or she had quit drinking, wouldn't that be a powerful message to another alcoholic still struggling to find the way to admit the same thing?

And, if such a statement would be a powerful message at a gathering like Freedom Fest, why wouldn't it be even more powerful if broadcast on a well-produced and well-scripted television show?

Of course it would be, Jorgenson told himself. This was exactly the kind of program he'd been searching for, and it seemed to be all but falling right into his lap. The event would take place at Metropolitan Stadium, where the popular Minnesota Vikings football team and Minnesota Twins baseball team played their home games. What a perfect setting that would be.

He could see himself now, walking over the deep turf of Met Stadium, seeking out one celebrity after another, easily persuading each of them to agree to go on camera and tell a story of drinking and recovery. Successful people in recovery ought to have just the upbeat message he wanted, and the interviews would fly by. After all, these were people accustomed to being in the public eye.

A wave of doubt washed over his optimistic dreaming for a moment.

What if he couldn't pull it off? What if these celebrities, pushed and pulled from all sides every day to speak out for this or that cause, just said they didn't want to do it this time? Why should a big-name personality sit down with the director of an alcohol treatment center in Pierre, South

Dakota? Especially when the director of that center was promising a big-time production but hadn't done anything quite like this in his life?

What if the celebrities said, "Show me your film credits," or "Name a couple of documentaries you've done and tell me where they were broadcast," or "Tell me the names of a few other celebrities you've had on your program."

Those were knotty concerns, and Jorgenson had to admit to himself that it was entirely possible he'd have no luck at all in this venture. But he continued to hold the Freedom Fest flyer in his hand, and the vision of a television show focusing on celebrities' personal stories of recovery grew stronger.

Didn't the Big Book of Alcoholics Anonymous advise recovering alcoholics to share their stories to help others? The simple formula outlined in that wise old book—what it was like, what happened and what it's like now—was exactly the approach Jorgenson had been seeking.

He pushed his doubts aside. This felt so right.

He'd been gradually learning in sobriety to trust his feelings. That hadn't worked in the drinking days, not at all. Too many times he'd trusted feelings that grew from selfishness or anger or resentment. The motives were all messed up, and the feelings came out skewed.

Since he'd gotten sober, though, and especially since he'd begun trying in earnest to seek God's will in all his actions, he'd gotten better at sorting out those emotions and identifying the kinds of feelings that said, "This is a good thing, not for you personally but for people who need help." That was the feeling he was experiencing as he thought about the shows he could put together with the cooperation of the people at Freedom Fest.

The more he reflected, the more he got the clear message: This just feels like something that was meant to happen. And, even though he had yet to do a single interview, had yet to get a foot of exposed film in the can, had yet to sign one agreement with a station to air the material once he finished it, Jorgenson laughed as he thought of the perfect title for the shows he could see resulting from the Freedom Fest.

It's Great To Be Alive. The same title as the River Park motto. It would tie in with all the other public awareness efforts the center sponsored. It would carry exactly the right message of hope and joy. It felt just right.

So, with a title and a vision of a way to spread the message of recovery, how could he fail?

Besides, he told himself, what's the worst that can happen?

"Maybe I go up there and fall flat on my face," he said to himself. "Well, I've done that before. Besides, even if I get there and get turned down by every big name in the entire baseball park, I'd be no worse off than I am now. And what if a couple of them agree to talk? What if just one of those people will share his story? Wouldn't that be worth making the effort?"

He knew it would. He could get people to agree to tell their stories. Of course he could. They'd want to do it, once they realized this was a serious program aimed at suffering alcoholics and not some fly-by-night group trying to take advantage of a big name. They'd welcome an opportunity to carry the message of recovery to a whole new audience.

As he made the arrangements to be in Minneapolis, accompanied by a film crew from KELO-TV, Jorgenson dreamed of an expanded program. *It's Great To Be Alive* would be much more than this one-time visit to Freedom Fest. It could be an ongoing program, a series of regularly scheduled programs dealing with alcoholism. Nobody had ever done anything like that before.

And, if he could get personalities and celebrities to tell their stories on camera, why couldn't he invite them to visit River Park itself? If people of influence came to the center and saw how successful the program of treatment was, they could tell others, and the help for alcoholics would spread far beyond the hedges of the city park in Pierre and far past the banks of the Missouri River in the middle of South Dakota.

A Minneapolis businessman named Wheelock Whitney, instrumental in the preparations and coordination of the entire Freedom Fest event, also offered invaluable help to River Park's film crew. He encouraged Jorgenson in his plans and promised to have several recovering alcoholics available for interviews. He was as good as his word. When Jorgenson and the film crew set up their equipment in a small room inside the stadium, the celebrities began to roll in.

Outside, in the expanse of a stadium that usually hosted major-league baseball on bright summer afternoons, 25,000 people talked about alcoholism and listened to others, sharing their experiences, strength and hope.

Inside the makeshift film studio, famous people with instantly recognizable names and faces did the same thing, telling Jorgenson some of their most personal stories of drunkenness and of recovery.

"As long as I live, I'll remember the awe I felt after the first interview was finished," Jorgenson said. "I'd been nervous as a cat. You have doubts just before you begin something like this, and I had them. Was I prepared for this? Would I be able to draw them out? What did I think I was doing here, anyway? It's funny now, but I really was jittery, nervous and a little frightened, but as excited as a little kid, too. I knew what an opportunity I'd been given."

Dick Van Dyke came in first. A veteran performer with a background as a song-and-dance man, he was the star of his own long-running television series, the featured talent in a show loaded with that commodity. Jorgenson had laughed at the antics and predicaments of Rob Petrie, Van Dyke's television character, and of his on-screen wife, Laura, played by Mary Tyler Moore.

The man who walked into the filming room that day looked like the television star, but he acted like a country kid on his first trip to town. The boisterous, slapstick, funny man from television was nowhere to be found. The man sitting across a small coffee table from Jorgenson was reserved, almost shy, as if he'd never faced an audience in his life. Dressed in a pair of dark slacks and a sky-blue, short-sleeved golf shirt, Van Dyke seemed to want to be cooperative. He just didn't have much to say, not at first.

Jorgenson was taken aback.

"I guess I'd expected the celebrities to carry the conversation," he says. "Put a question out there, and let them talk. I'd worried about ways to keep the interviews down to a manageable time, so we could talk with a lot of people. I don't know that it ever occurred to me a television star might be hard to talk with."

Perhaps it was just that the experience was nearly as new for Van Dyke as it was for Jorgenson. As the questions moved from the problems that drinking had caused to the change in his life that sobriety had wrought, Van Dyke grew more and more animated. His eyes lit up as he told Jorgenson, "My worst day now is better than my best day then."

Decades later, that line remains one Jorgenson always remembers from the first "shoot" in the *It's Great To Be Alive* series. It's one that gave hundreds upon hundreds of alcoholics a real ray of hope when the Van Dyke interview was shown as part of their River Park treatment.

Van Dyke also told Jorgenson that day that people don't understand recovery from alcoholism if they think it means returning to the way life was before the drinking began. The truth was, he said, he'd recovered much more than just his pre-drinking self.

"Life is more than just coping," he said. "It's an exciting adventure and growth."

Next up that day was Garry Moore, the sharp-witted theater and television star who told the wonderfully funny and sad story of the woman whose daughter couldn't be an alcoholic because she'd been a debutante.

Moore came on more the way Jorgenson had expected. He kept the conversation moving, interjecting jokes, poking fun at himself, and still managing to convey a powerful message of hope for suffering alcoholics if they were only willing to take a chance and reach out for help.

It was Moore who told Jorgenson that being a TV star didn't prevent him from being a raging alcoholic. It just meant he had a big house to go home to when he was drunk.

He talked freely about his drinking years and admitted that not drinking had been difficult in the early going. It seemed like such a negative thing, he said, like he was losing something important.

"But after you get used to the idea that you can get through 24 hours without a drink, accumulate enough 24 hours and you begin to say to yourself, 'Hey, this is something I no longer have to have,'" Moore said. "It becomes a positive experience. And the marvelous thing about it is that it's the most positive thing in my life now."

Moore looked into the camera and declared that alcoholism can be treated; the progression of the disease can be arrested. "I'm stronger now, I'm happier than I've ever been."

One of Jorgenson's next guests that day was a real surprise.

Fran Tarkenton, scrambling quarterback for the Minnesota Vikings, walked into the room, ready to talk about alcoholism and what it had cost friends of his in the world of professional sports. Tarkenton didn't have a drinking problem himself, but he said athletes have a chance to be role models for young people, and if a message about what alcohol can do might turn a teen-ager or young adult away from that path, he wanted to help.

Tarkenton's all-out style of play at quarterback had made him one of the upper Midwest's biggest sports heroes. His fame wasn't limited to the Twin Cities market, though. He'd done some of his highlight-reel dipping and dodging for the New York Giants before being traded to the Vikings. He was known across the country, and he was in front of the KELO-TV camera, talking with Jorgenson.

Tarkenton brought a new dimension to the discussion that day. Not an alcoholic, he turned some of the conversation to the way alcoholics affect the lives of those around them. Whether most people know it, he said (and in 1976 people were only beginning to realize the truth of what he would say) almost everyone's life has been touched by an alcoholic.

He offered a straightforward plea for anyone who had a drinking problem or anyone who cared about an alcoholic to reach out for the help available at places like River Park.

"Some of us stumble, some of us fall, but it's easier to get up when there's a helping hand and someone who cares," Tarkenton said that day.

Jorgenson corralled a couple of other big-name professional athletes that day.

Don Newcombe, a pitcher for the old Brooklyn Dodgers, told him, "I've been sick. I'm well now. I want people to see how good I look and how good I feel."

Ryne Duren, the New York Yankees hurler with the coke-bottle spectacles and the flame-throwing right arm, talked of education and the role that recovering alcoholics can play in that. He had left the world of big-league baseball to become director of a treatment program in Wisconsin.

"Knowing and understanding, we become educators, and we have to address ourselves to the meaningful people around the alcoholic," Duren said.

∗ ∗ ∗

Back in South Dakota, working with the KELO-TV crew on film editing and scripting for the shows, Jorgenson could barely contain his excitement. Meaningful comments from one celebrity after another ran through his mind non-stop. Their words contained so many of the messages he'd been trying to tell the clients at River Park, and now, finally, there was a chance to get that word out over television.

The first half-hour program in the *It's Great To Be Alive* series, a show featuring Dick Van Dyke, hit the air on New Year's Eve, 1976. It may not stop a lot of holiday revelers from going out and drinking, a friend told Jorgenson when he heard the time and date. "But, if they have a problem, it's sure going to mess up any fun they were thinking of having. They'll see themselves right on camera in everything Van Dyke says."

Five stations agreed to air the program. Their combined broadcast signals sent the program to virtually every populated area of South Dakota. The show spilled across the state's borders, too, to eastern Wyoming, southeastern North Dakota, northeast Nebraska and western Minnesota and Iowa.

"I've had a lot of people tell me there was never a show quite like that," Jorgenson said. "I know that in my research and work in the field, I'd not encountered anything similar. And the response was fantastic."

The telephones at River Park began to ring before the first program concluded. The calls varied—a woman crying because her husband was already out getting drunk on that New Year's Eve, a lonely-sounding man who wondered if he could talk to someone about a "friend of mine who sometimes seems to lose control of his drinking," a teen-aged girl wondering if there were any way she could get help for her mother, who seemed to drink herself into unconsciousness four or five afternoons a week.

Jorgenson had had big dreams about how the program might carry a message, but even his optimism hadn't matched the power of that first broadcast.

"It was clear we'd touched a terribly raw nerve with the show," he said. "The continued flow of telephone calls to the center's staff showed we'd succeeded in getting public attention."

The new year was barely a few hours old when Jorgenson sat down to begin writing the script for a second *It's Great To Be Alive*.

In coming years, the show would feature a broad spectrum of personalities and public figures, from former First Lady Betty Ford to country singer Johnny Cash to *Kids Say The Darnedest Things* host Art Linkletter. Schuller did a show. So did Brooke Shields and Ralph Waite and Lawrence Welk.

One of Glenn Jorgenson's favorite stories was told by Art Linkletter.

"I was interviewing a 6-year-old boy," Linkletter said. "I asked him to name his favorite Bible story, and he said 'Humpty Dumpty.' I replied that I was the son of a preacher and I knew there was nothing in the Bible about Humpty Dumpty. 'Oh yes there is!' he said. 'Humpty Dumpty was an egg and one day he fell down and was busted into a million pieces and only God could put him back together.'"

That story, Jorgenson thought, was a perfect explanation of what often happened at River Park.

Sports figures continued to be drawn to the forum. Big Carl Eller from the Vikings had a particularly strong message. A second generation of baseball stars shared their stories, too, people like Bob Welch and Greg Gagne.

Sometimes the interviews took place locally. Other times, Jorgenson and the film crew traveled, as was the case when they interviewed Betty Ford at her home in California.

Jorgenson's approach to getting celebrities to do the program was to find one, walk up, and ask. The Johnny Cash interview came about that way. Knowing that Cash would be at the South Dakota State Fair for a Labor Day performance, Jorgenson drove to Mitchell, a town 25 miles from the fairgrounds, where the entertainer and his troupe were staying. Cash wasn't around, but the staffer traveling with Jorgenson that day recognized the lead guitar player from the band.

The staffer had grown up watching Cash and the Tennessee Three, and he'd noticed when this young guitar picker had filled the spot in the band that once belonged to legendary Luther Perkins. The staffer complimented the musician on his guitar work. He introduced Jorgenson, and together they talked of why they'd driven to Mitchell on a holiday afternoon. Cash's guitar picker led them into the motel lunchroom and introduced them to Cash's road manager. The manager appeared more than a little bit put out about having a quiet lunch interrupted. He took the proffered information about the TV shows and promised to have Cash read it when the tour ended. He went back to eating his lunch of charbroiled chicken, while Jorgenson and his staffer hit the highway back to Pierre and River Park.

It took almost two years, but Cash eventually wound up in front of the camera. The program was dynamite.

Most of the shows were spellbinding, and most of the celebrities Jorgenson sought out committed to the interviews.

"If you could get to them with a real understanding of what the show was all about, they were eager to do it," he said.

Each time another celebrity shared a story of alcoholism and recovery, a new show aired and the telephones at River Park rang and rang. Jorgenson knew he'd found the public awareness vehicle he'd been seeking.

He was also grateful for the enthusiastic support he received from the media. Newspapers and radio stations throughout the region promoted the series, and the show, while it was produced by KELO-TV, was broadcast by several other television stations.

"It would take time," he said. "But each program was bringing a little more awareness, a little more understanding. I knew the result would be acceptance, and that would mean more people would find the help we had to offer. The future looked limitless."

It was at the 1976 Freedom Fest in Minneapolis that the first celebrities were interviewed for the television series It's Great To Be Alive. The Freedom Fest was a celebration for recovering addicts from all over the world. A huge crowd filled the Minnesota Vikings stadium in Bloomington, and a host of movie stars, celebrities, and national personalities were part of the program.

Behind the scenes at the Freedom Fest, a television crew from KELO-TV in Sioux Falls filmed celebrities talking about how alcoholism had affected their lives. Maxine Krogh (left) was the first producer of the It's Great To Be Alive series, and Jim Keith (center) was writer and director. Ann Parker (right) produced the show in later years.

Comedian and actor Dick Van Dyke was the first celebrity to be interviewed for It's Great To Be Alive. "Anyone—no matter how successful—can be an alcoholic," he said.

Garry Moore, theater and television star, assured viewers that alcoholism can be treated.

The Rev. Robert Schuller, minister at the Crystal Cathedral and Hour of Power televangelist, appeared on two It's Great To Be Alive shows.

First Lady Betty Ford was gracious,
responsive and inspiring when Jorgenson
interviewed her in the president's office
in Rancho Mirage, California. She
talked candidly about her treatment for
breast cancer as well as her struggles with
addictions. She established the Betty Ford
Center for the treatment of chemical
dependency in 1982.

Model and actress Brooke Shields was
never an alcoholic herself, but she told
viewers how she had been affected by her
mother's alcoholism.

Actress Cheryl Ladd appeared on the River Park TV program to help people understand how the disease of alcoholism affects the children of an alcoholic. Born in Huron, South Dakota, she gained fame through her role on the TV drama Charlie's Angels.

Claudia Black, Ph.D. (at right), a social psychologist, talked about the effects of alcoholism on children when she taped an interview for It's Great To Be Alive. Children quickly learn to deny what is happening, she said.

Joe Foss (left), World War II hero, former South Dakota Governor and head of the American Football League, told the It's Great To Be Alive audience about the prevalence of addiction problems among professional athletes.

Veteran actor and songwriter Clifton Davis (right) told viewers that children need to be the focus of future efforts to stop drug and alcohol abuse.

Leonard Firestone (below), a former U.S. Ambassador to Belgium, helped Betty Ford establish the Betty Ford Center for alcoholism treatment. He and his wife Nicky (left) were also enthusiastic supporters of River Park, and were interviewed in 1985 for It's Great To Be Alive.

Singer Johnny Cash (above) told viewers about his spiritual experience that caused him to curtail his drug addiction. He had passed out in the Nickajack Cave, a tourist attraction in Tennessee, when he woke up, felt God's presence in his heart and was able to struggle out to safety.

Country singer Larry Gatlin (left) told viewers how he became addicted to cocaine, and how he eventually sought treatment when he realized drugs were ruining his life.

Lawrence Welk was at the height of his popularity when he appeared on It's Great To Be Alive to urge viewers to seek help for addictions.

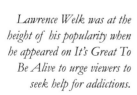

White Eagle, the Native American (Lakota Sioux) gospel singer and operatic tenor, appeared on the show twice. The first time he told viewers about his strong need for belonging that led to his alcoholism, how treatment helped him overcome the addiction, and how his life had been enriched since he quit drinking. His second appearance on the show was after he had been diagnosed with AIDS. White Eagle died in 1995, about six weeks after his 39th birthday.

Because he suspected his daughter's suicide was related to her use of LSD, television personality Art Linkletter (above) was happy to speak out about the dangers of drug use on It's Great To Be Alive.

Ralph Waite (left), actor and director, is best-known for his portrayal of John Walton on the television series The Waltons. He said his role as a hardworking and responsible Depression-era father caused him to confront his own alcoholism.

Congressman Wilbur Mills and his wife Polly were interviewed for It's Great To Be Alive. Mills said that at one time his alcoholism was so bad that he would forget what he had discussed with the president in the Oval Office. He'd have to read the next day's New York Times in order to discover what statements he had made.

Charlie Plumb spent six years in a prisoner of war camp in Vietnam. On It's Great To Be Alive, he drew parallels between his experiences in captivity and the challenges faced by alcohol and drug users.

Actress Susan Sullivan, who gained fame while starring in the television series Falcon Crest, told viewers about her father's alcoholism and how important it is for family members to realize how they are being affected.

At the time she appeared on It's Great To Be Alive, Michele Lee was starring in Knots Landing, a popular television show. One of the storylines of the show was based on her character's addiction to prescription painkiller drugs.

Tom Brokaw, television journalist, author, and a native South Dakotan, lent his support to River Park and its efforts to publicize the disease of alcoholism so that people would be encouraged to seek help.

Dave Dedrick, a recovering alcoholic and South Dakota television personality, provided many public service announcements for the It's Great To Be Alive program. He is shown here arm-wrestling with Carl Eller, who gained fame as a defensive end for the Minnesota Vikings. Eller was also a recovering alcoholic.

Helene Duhammel (right), a television journalist in Rapid City, told It's Great To Be Alive viewers about how a positive attitude can help alcoholics recover, just as she had used positive thinking during her treatment for cancer.

Joan Kroc was keenly interested in treatment programs for alcohol and drug addictions. She visited River Park several times, appeared on It's Great To Be Alive, and received the River Park "Friend of the Alcoholic" award.

Several famous athletes appeared on It's Great To Be Alive. Pro-football player Rosie Grier talked about his work with inner-city youth in the Los Angeles area.

Bob Welch, a starting pitcher for the LA Dodgers and the Oakland Athletics, described his struggle with alcoholism—as did another well-known pitcher, Don Newcombe.

Fran Tarkenton, a quarterback for the Minnesota Vikings, told how friends and family had been affected by alcohol and drugs.

Pitcher Ryne Duren (left) and shortstop Greg Gagne were among other sport celebrities who appeared on the program.

River Park earned the support of many prominent government figures. In addition to several other South Dakota governors, Walter Miller (above right) and Bill Janklow (above left) praised River Park's efforts. Janklow called River Park "the Mount Rushmore of alcoholism treatment." While he was in office, South Dakota Governor Harvey Wollman brought his family to the River Park facility in Pierre to sing Christmas songs for the people receiving treatment.

Under Governor Nils Boe (above left), Jorgenson was the state's director of employment and learned how alcoholism can affect employers. Governor Richard Kneip (top right) co-chaired a fundraising drive for River Park, and appointed Jorgenson to the South Dakota Commission on Alcoholism. Governor George Mickelson (bottom right) appointed Jorgenson to the state board of Vocational Education and was an enthusiastic supporter of River Park and its programs.

South Dakota's Congressional delegates were also supporters of River Park. Senator
Larry Pressler (top left) and Senator Tom Daschle (top right) visited River Park several
times; in Washington, D.C., the Jorgensons were guests of Senator Jim Abnor in the
Senate Dining Room.

Senator George McGovern with Phyllis and Glenn Jorgenson and their daughter Jennifer. Senator McGovern appeared on It's Great To Be Alive to talk about his daughter Terry, who had died as a result of her alcoholism.

The Jorgensons with McDonald's founder Ray Kroc, another prominent supporter of River Park.

Senator Larry Pressler (right) with Walter Burke, father of River Park co-founder Shanard Burke. Walter made the first $50 donation to River Park.

Every year, River Park honored several people with awards. Staff members were recognized for outstanding work with "Heart" awards; an "Alumni of the Year" award was presented. River Park's "Friend of the Alcoholic" (FOA) award honored people who in some significant way had supported treatment centers and programs.

Friend of the Alcoholic' award recipients Lloyd and Gladys Jorgenson (Glenn's parents).

"Friend of the Alcoholic" award recipients Clarence and Carol Anderson (Phyllis's parents).

KELO broadcasting executives Joe Floyd (above right) and Evans Nord (right) received River Park "Friend of the Alcoholic" awards. Floyd's award was presented by Ted Muenster.

Board chairman Shanard Burke presented "Friend of the Alcoholic" awards to Florence Parr, widow of River Park co-founder Jack Parr, and George Specker, a contractor who helped design and oversaw renovations at the River Park facilities.

More River Park "Friend of the Alcoholic" recipients: Bill Murphy (top left), a frequent lecturer at the treatment centers; Del Ripley (top right), a Gettysburg businessman; and Jackie Lofgren (below), KELO public affairs director.

Kay Reardon (top photo), Ray Sjodin (center) and "Tiny" Fiedler also received "Friend of the Alcoholic" awards for their enthusiastic support of River Park.

Glenn Jorgenson's contributions to the state were recognized in 1996 when he was inducted into the South Dakota Hall of Fame. In 2002, Carol Regier of the Keystone Treatment Center presented Jorgenson with the Mitzi Carroll Achievement Award in recognition of outstanding service in the field of chemical dependency.

Phyllis Jorgenson with Lois Wilson, the founder of Al-Anon and the widow of the founder of Alcoholics Anonymous. They were in Chicago, attending the premier of an educational film about alcoholism that was produced by Joan Kroc.

Phyllis and Glenn Jorgenson

Chapter Ten

The Family Program

Yes, in many ways the future did look unlimited.

Alcoholic men and women kept showing up at River Park's door, asking for help, willing to go to any lengths to escape their addiction. Those same men and women continued to leave their treatment program with a solid grasp of the principles of sobriety and a promise that, so long as they continued to work on the program of recovery, they'd find that, truly, "It's Great To Be Alive." Those men and women of River Park continued to astound their families, friends, bosses and co-workers with their changed attitudes.

The money worries had been eased—not eliminated, not by a long shot, but at least eased—by the acceptance of alcohol treatment as something health insurance companies should recognize and fund for policy holders.

That decision would prove to be a mixed blessing for the chemical-dependency field. The availability of insurance coverage opened the door to treatment for many people who might otherwise not have been able to afford it. It was one more avenue to treatment, and it was one more excuse taken away from the alcoholic who, upon telling others he'd go to treatment except that he couldn't pay, would be told, "Your insurance will cover most of it."

At the same time, the presence of third-party sources of financing and the reliability of their payments once the treatment center had been approved was among factors that drove costs of treatment higher. It wasn't the only pressure, but it was among them, and over the course of the next decade or so, the cost of a month-long stay in some treatment centers doubled and tripled.

River Park held the line when and where it could. Jorgenson maintained a belief that treatment centers had to maintain a price level that wouldn't put them out of consideration of any individual or family in need. If insurance coverage was available for a client, fine.

If independent sources of revenue were available, fine, too. If no money could be found anywhere and an alcoholic stood at the door ready to commit to the program of recovery, Jorgenson and his staff looked again, and then again. They believed the individual stood there ready to make a change by the grace of God. If that was so, the means to finance the treatment program must be available. And so they searched.

The money to keep the doors open and the staff working came from a variety of sources. Some clients had their own resources or simply borrowed the money. The state office of vocational rehabilitation provided financial support for some of the people it referred to River Park. A few employers had advanced a good worker the cost of treatment, and a growing number of insurance carriers had begun to pay part or all of the costs. And, the donations and gifts continued to be a key to paying for treatment when someone asked for help and flat out didn't have any other way to pay.

Without any federal or state money to help cover costs, Jorgenson scrambled each day to find people and groups willing to contribute. The task was wearying, requiring travel, speaking engagements and ongoing attention, but Jorgenson rarely considered it a burden. The alternative, government funding, would have meant accepting government regulations and controls. Jorgenson wanted to maintain the flexibility to change and adapt programs to meet the needs of clients.

Change could come quickly at River Park in those early years. If staff members noticed a recurring need in treatment or if a suggested improvement in the program began to be heard in more and more conversations with clients, River Park could give the idea a try. No grant writing, no feasibility studies, no justifying the proposal to a federal agency or state board.

"It was easy to try something under those conditions," Jorgenson said. "If it worked the way you wanted it to, you could keep doing it. If it flopped, you could just quit doing it and either go back to the way things had been done before or try something else new. It was a pretty informal operation, pretty hands-on. But we kept discovering that it was also pretty effective."

With all that going for the program, Glenn Jorgenson still wasn't satisfied. Much more remained to be done.

He'd been learning far too much about the disease of alcoholism to become complacent, in spite of the success of the treatment program. What he'd learned, in the workshops he attended regularly, the conversations he had with other experts in the field, and the informal chats every single day with River Park clients, was that a desperate need wasn't being met. The need was to reach out and help families of alcoholics. In far too many cases, they were crying out with no one to hear them.

Some family members tried to get help on their own. Al-Anon chapters had existed in most cities for decades. Members of Al-Anon followed their own 12-step program of recovery, helping each other accept that they, too, were powerless over alcoholism. The program tried to tell the spouse, the children, the parents, that they weren't responsible for the alcoholic's drinking. They weren't to blame. They didn't cause it. Whether or not it continued didn't depend on their actions. While they were unable to stop the alcoholic's drinking, though, they could focus their energies on attitudes and actions that would prevent drinking from destroying their lives.

It's a hard message for the wife or child of an alcoholic to understand, even harder to accept. The business of living with an alcoholic becomes such an ingrained part of their lives that nothing else feels normal.

Claudia Black, Ph.D., a social psychologist, has worked with children of alcoholics for years. She says that the denial system that allows such children to function in the abnormality of a home controlled by chemical dependency appears at an early age.

"We find that, by the time they're 9 years old, children have a denial system," Black told Jorgenson during a taping of the television series. "One of the things they're learning is that it's not okay to trust."

The defenses go up, she said. There's no consistency, no guarantee of follow-through on actions, promises, discipline or daily decisions.

"They're children who live with a lot of broken promises," Black says. "In an alcoholic family, we do what we need to do in order to survive…It's not okay to feel."

Brooke Shields knows how that feels. She grew up in an alcoholic home, and even though she became a child star as an actor and matured into a beautiful young woman who always appeared poised and self-confident in public, she says she spent her childhood in total confusion and still struggles as an adult to understand what happened and how it affected her.

"There's a feeling of constantly walking on eggshells," Shields said when she appeared on *It's Great To Be Alive*. "You see the whole system around you breaking down."

As a teen-ager with a mother who drank uncontrollably, Brooke Shields found herself making the decisions in the family. She had to grow up without being an adult. She never knew whether she'd find her mother alert or passed out when she got home after school or a movie. The most perfect day of her high school years could be ruined in a moment.

"I was a kid. I didn't know what to do. It was like living in complete uncertainty," she said. "The day was fine, because I wasn't home. But when three or four o'clock rolled around, I'd be afraid to go home."

She lived with anger at her mother for not getting a grip on her drinking. She also lived with fear of what might happen next. Always she lived with guilt. Was there something she should have done that she failed to do? Was she doing something that she shouldn't?

"The games that were played were so intense," she said.

Brooke Shields would agree that a sickness existed in her childhood home. Her mother's drinking created much of the problem, but her own response to it also nurtured the abnormal behavior.

Her description of living with an alcoholic strongly supports the often-reported statement that family members become as sick or sicker than the alcoholic.

Today, that statement might seem obvious to the experts in chemical dependency. When River Park and a very few other treatment programs were doing the ground-breaking work with family programs in the early 1970s though, much less was known about how families were affected by alcoholism and how they could be helped toward recovery.

The thing that made the issue of such importance was, as Claudia Black said, "For every person who has a drinking problem, four or five other people are affected."

Jorgenson recognized that intuitively. But he'd been so focused on getting a treatment center up and running and on finding the public awareness programs that would spread understanding and education beyond the walls of the center; he'd had little time to really study the family nature of the disease.

"First things first," a time-honored AA slogan advised. And Jorgenson had known that primary treatment was first. Public acceptance was critical. But, with his treatment center operating a successful program and with the television series off to a solid start, the needs of family members had to be addressed.

At the time, the topic was only beginning to make its way into the discussions of alcoholism. Here and there, at a workshop in Boston or a chemical dependency conference in Denver, the word began to get out that family members needed help, as much or more than alcoholics did. Some of the speakers in the field were beginning to use the "sick or sicker" phrase as they traveled the country talking about the disease.

What to do about families of alcoholics? It wasn't an easy topic for Jorgenson. It wasn't an easy topic for many alcoholics.

Even if an alcoholic had come to accept his powerlessness over alcohol, the lack of control in his life and the need to change, it was a painful step beyond that to recognizing and accepting the way his drinking had affected others in his family.

It was one thing to admit the drinking had messed up the alcoholic's life. It was something else to accept that the drinking had messed up the lives of people around him.

Acceptance of that fact seldom came easily to the family members, either.

After all, hadn't the wife compensated for her husband's binges and blackouts and hangovers by working twice as hard, by being twice the parent? She wasn't the one who wrecked the car or got into the fight at the bar. She was the one who stretched the money to pay the bills, who rushed from work to fix supper and get groceries and make sure one of the parents got to the PTA meeting or the ballet recital or the Little League game. She was managing just fine, thank you, if only he would straighten up and quit drinking.

But she wasn't doing fine, and neither were the children. Jorgenson learned that first-hand, from Phyllis, during one of the many times she brought up the topic of family treatment in the early days of River Park's operation.

Phyllis had gently pushed for some kind of family involvement almost from the beginning. She was a regular at Al-Anon, and she knew how desperately some spouses battled to keep their family going. They needed to know much more about the disease of alcoholism, she told Jorgenson. Even a day set aside for family members would be a beginning to understanding how the disease had affected them. Perhaps they could view the same films as the alcoholics in treatment, listen to some of the same records and tapes and lectures.

Sure, she said, some of the family members were going to Al-Anon and to AlaTeen. But some of the alcoholics in treatment had gone to AA, too. If treatment based on the principles of AA worked so well for so many alcoholics, didn't it stand to reason that a family program that incorporated the principles of Al-Anon would help family members?

And, Phyllis told Jorgenson, she knew just how each of those spouses felt, because she'd felt that way herself when he was drinking, and even when he was in treatment.

"I remember how I felt when you went to treatment and how much I needed some help and there wasn't any available," she told him. "I felt like nobody cared about me. And I see that in so many women that I know. They are angry and resentful that their husbands get 30 days of treatment and they get no help at all."

Jorgenson knew she was right. The need certainly existed. And, in the region for sure, no one else was meeting the need. A River Park family program would fill a gap in the whole-person approach to treatment. Wouldn't the chances of long-term recovery improve for the alcoholic and the family members alike if everyone were working a program based on spiritual principles such as those found in the 12 steps of Alcoholics Anonymous? It could hardly be otherwise.

But was this the right time for River Park?

It wasn't that long ago that meeting each payroll was a struggle. It wasn't that long ago the clients were listening to only a few scratchy old "Father John Doe" long-playing records. Was the basic inpatient program strong enough so that Jorgenson could turn his efforts toward a family program?

And, regardless of how firmly he believed the River Park program had an element of divine inspiration, these things didn't just fall out of the big-leafed elm and cottonwood trees along the Missouri River.

A family program required space of its own. Where would that be found in a converted convent already so packed with people and program materials it threatened to burst through the brick walls. A family program meant more than a wife or a husband, for sure. It meant parents, grandparents if they could be convinced to attend, and children. Getting the children involved would be a crucial step for a successful program.

"That was going to be the noisy part in all of this, but how could you try to help set a family on a course of recovery without getting the children right in the middle of everything?" Jorgenson wondered. "Include them and you need more space, and probably more staff. But if you leave them out, it might look to them like one more big family secret that they weren't being told. We had to have them in every phase of the family program."

And, perhaps as important as any other question, who would run such a program? Where would a treatment center find an individual with the qualifications to design, create and run a program of family treatment for chemical dependency? The field was so new. There simply were no experts, at least none with any experience.

Valid questions, every one of them. And if Jorgenson had waited until he was sure of the answer to each one, River Park might never have developed its family program. As luck, or divine guidance, would have it, he didn't wait that long.

Not long after he had sat and listened to Phyllis make her impassioned case for family treatment, Jorgenson found himself talking about the subject at a public meeting. He'd been thinking about it frequently during the days at the center and evenings at home, and he'd found himself recalling some of the ways his drinking had hurt his family.

Maybe it was because those reflections produced such sharp emotions in Jorgenson that he could almost relive the incidents he remembered. Maybe he'd had a message from a Higher Power that this was an important next step. Or, maybe it was simply the right time to talk about this subject in public.

For whatever reason, without planning it ahead of time and without really realizing he was doing it, Jorgenson began to tell the audience at a public meeting a bit of the story of how his alcoholism had hurt his family and of the obvious need they had for the kind of help he'd received in treatment.

The response was overwhelmingly positive. People stopped as they left the room to thank him for speaking so openly and with such feeling. Others paused to encourage Jorgenson, and through him, River Park, to take the lead in meeting the needs of families.

The reaction left Jorgenson both excited and humbled.

Clearly, a family program would find widespread support, enough to assure its success financially, if staff and material could be found to assure its effectiveness as education and treatment. That was exciting, and Jorgenson could hardly wait to begin the step-by-step planning and the detail work that would bring the program into being.

At the same time, he felt almost, well, unworthy. While he'd worked so hard to bring help to alcoholics and to bring awareness to the profession and the public, he suddenly felt that he'd failed to give the family the same attention. He needed to redouble his efforts in this area.

He remembered numerous times when he'd told a bit of his drinking story to a newcomer and had downplayed the impact his alcoholism might have had on his wife and children. He'd believed it was enough that he'd generally been able to feed and clothe and shelter them, and that he hadn't beaten them or humiliated them, hadn't run off as some alcoholics did, hadn't shown up drunk at their recitals and plays as other alcoholics did.

But he hadn't given enough thought to the atmosphere his drinking had created in the household and how that affected the children and their relationships with him and with their mother. What about the inconsistencies in actions, the broken promises and the other actions that taught family members to hold back feelings, to keep secrets, to build walls around their emotions? If all that he'd learned about the effects of alcoholism was true, his own family had become sick while he'd sunk further and further into his own illness.

He thanked God for giving him that insight, and he prayed for guidance in developing a strong, effective family program and for strength to build it.

"Lord, if it would fit your plan, help me to get this important program in place and running as quickly as possible, so that not even one more family needs to suffer through the misery of an alcoholic relationship without the help that could be available," he whispered.

✳ ✳ ✳

With the decision to start a family program behind him, Jorgenson was anxious to get into action. He couldn't wait to tell Phyllis. All those conversations, all that urging, finally she'd see that it was paying off. He slipped the topic casually into a conversation with her the next day at his corner office in River Park.

"I need your help on something," he said. "I've been thinking of this for a while, and I'm not sure how to start. If we were going to offer a family program here at River Park, what's the first thing we'd need to do?"

Phyllis stared at him, her eyes wide. She searched his face, looking for any sign that this might just be his way of teasing. But he didn't look like a man who was joking. What he looked like more than anything else was a guy who was trying to contain a great feeling of excitement. And, as the realization sank in that her husband was serious about a program that had been her dream since River Park began, Phyllis Jorgenson knew she must look much the same way.

"Oh, my," Phyllis said, her voice almost lost in a surprised intake of breath.

"You mean it, don't you," she said. "Oh, yes, you do. This will be one of the best things you've ever done here at River Park. How do we get started?"

Jorgenson laughed. "I asked you first. How do we get started? What's the very first thing we need to do if we're going to put together the best family program ever?"

Excitement blazed in Phyllis's eyes.

"Well, I'll have to think about this a bit," she said. "I mean, there's so much to be done, I'd hardly know where to begin. But it seems to me we'd be wise to check around and see if there are programs operating. Then we should travel to a few of them and see what kinds of facilities they have and what programs and materials. We'd need to look closely at how they get the clients and the families to interact. That's going to be important. I have some ideas about that I could share with whoever will run our program, but we should see what other people do, too."

"Yes," Jorgenson said, "I'd like you to share your ideas with the person who'll run our program. I have someone in mind who'd be just right."

Phyllis looked at him, waiting to hear his candidate.

"Would you do it, Phyll?" he asked. "Would you be in charge? I can't think of anyone I'd trust more to bring the sensitivity and energy and understanding to it that this program would need. We can find people to help, but I really think you should be in charge."

Phyllis hesitated for a moment, but only that long.

"Oh, I don't know if I could..." she said. "Could I? I'm not...Yes, I am. Of course. Yes, I want to do it."

Things moved quickly, once the initial decision had been made. Two new staff members were hired to work with Phyllis who, in a non-aggressive way, had begun to show that she intended to take charge of this program and make things happen.

A search of treatment programs across the country showed that a handful of them were offering family treatment. Minnesota seemed to be one of the leaders, as they were in developing inpatient treatment for chemical dependency. Phyllis, Glenn and the two new staffers traveled to their neighboring state to see what might work and what they should avoid.

They returned to River Park enthusiastic about the opportunities in this new venture. The whirlwind tour of family programs in Minnesota made them realize that a real key to success would be to get participation of as many family members as possible. It would also be important to make the family members understand that the program existed for them. The program wouldn't be some kind of alcoholic's auxiliary, aimed at supporting the alcoholic in treatment. Should that happen, it would be considered a big plus for the client, perhaps, but that wasn't the point.

No matter what happened to the client in treatment, the program Phyllis was putting together would be for the family members. It would be about their pain, their confusion, their anger, and, in the end, their recovery. That's why it would be so important that they participate.

Actress Susan Sullivan, who gained fame while starring in the television series *Falcon Crest*, understood how critical family recovery is in an alcoholic home. Her father drank when she was a child, and she learned early to find a place inside herself where she could stuff all the feelings and hurts.

"I could tell at a two-block distance which father was coming home," Sullivan recalled on an *It's Great To Be Alive* program. Just by his walk as he moved along the block toward the house, she knew whether her father would arrive sober and caring or drunk, abusive and embarrassing.

She grew up too early, almost skipping the emotional development of childhood.

"There's the feeling that you had to try to make things okay for your parents and your siblings," she said. "The feeling that you had to not have your *own* feelings."

It's been said that an alcoholic's emotional development is arrested when he or she begins to drink. That is, an alcoholic who begins to drink at age 16 doesn't develop emotionally beyond that as long as the drinking continues.

Those who work with families of alcoholics find a similar phenomenon at work. In an alcoholic relationship, the non-drinking members still have their emotions stunted. Much of the cause apparently is the secrecy that permeates every relationship, the feelings that can't be shared or even hinted at, the skewed and unreal world that develops.

Children of alcoholics, the social psychologist Claudia Black says, end up in adulthood with greater than normal instances of depression. They have trouble developing and nurturing relationships, and they have a higher than average likelihood of becoming chemically dependent themselves.

Once recovery begins, family members need time, treatment and care so they can let their emotions begin to develop again. Sullivan said it takes a long while before a child of an alcoholic is willing to open up. Long after the drinking has ended, the need for self-protection continues.

"You are still protecting yourself from something that's no longer a threat," she said.

Even with counseling and understanding, Sullivan said she finds herself retreating occasionally toward her old self. As a child, she often lived with the feeling that she wasn't very special, that she wasn't very important in her own home. The result was what she described as "a feeling that you want to roll yourself up in a little ball."

In Sullivan's case, which other children of alcoholics have said is an ideal description of how they often feel in adulthood, she said, "If it doesn't seem to be going well, I shut down."

Phyllis Jorgenson understood those feelings. She'd been there herself. That's one reason she worked so hard to persuade family members to participate in the River Park program while the alcoholic in their relationship was in treatment.

It wasn't always easy to convince the spouse or parents or children to get involved. Too many mixed feelings still got in the way.

"I don't need treatment," some would say. "If you can help my husband stop drinking, everything else will fall into place."

"I'm separated from the mean old drunk, and I'm sure not about to take my valuable time to do anything like that," others would growl. "If he gets help, fine, but I don't want any part of him."

Phyllis and the other family-program staff members gently prodded, suggesting that this time the focus wouldn't be on the alcoholic. It would be on the wife and her anger, on the children and their confusion, on the parents and their guilt.

"You aren't doing this for your spouse," Phyllis would say. "This isn't about him. You're doing it for you. And, trust me, you'll be grateful when the program is finished."

Family treatment began at River Park as a one-afternoon program, on Sundays. Jorgenson and the staff weren't a bit confident that family members would actually take time from jobs and weekday duties, so they tried to make the schedule intrude as little as possible into people's lives.

It took only a few sessions to realize that more time was needed to give family members a good start toward their own recovery and to realize that those family members would come. They'd come desperate for help, knowledge and understanding. Weekends, workdays, holidays—it didn't matter. The families were eager for help.

Soon the program was running Sunday, Monday and Tuesday, and it still wasn't enough. Expanding it to include Wednesday only increased the demand for more information and counseling sessions. Before long, the family program was a weeklong event, starting on Sunday afternoon, wrapping up late Friday.

Every family program ended with buckets of tears and long, fierce hugs as people who'd built emotional walls early in their lives finally broke through the barriers to touch their feelings and to revel in the mere fact that they could talk about their problems and fantasies and dreams with someone.

Classes ranged from communications skills to developing a spiritual foundation. For many family members, the River Park program was the first time anyone ever told them they weren't to blame for the alcoholic's behavior. If the son had gotten an A in geography or the daughter had made the basketball team or the wife had just not nagged so much, it wouldn't have kept the alcoholic from drinking. People who'd lived through the same kinds of fears and anger were telling these family members it wasn't their fault. They could set that burden down and never pick it up again.

The relief that news brought the families could be seen in their suddenly shining eyes, in the way their heads came up and their shoulders squared, and most of all, in the laughter that filled the rooms by the last day of the program.

"We've given you the tools," Phyllis would say in the closing session. "Now it's up to you to do the work. You can be happy."

Glenn Jorgenson tried to attend the closing sessions of the family programs whenever a scheduling conflict didn't interfere. He felt a tremendous spiritual surge as he watched the women and men and children hug Phyllis and the other staff members. He sat in the back of the room sometimes and tried to pick out the family members he'd seen only a few days earlier. They'd been so changed that sometimes it was difficult to recognize them.

"In almost every class from the family program, I could find one or more people who were like that woman we talked about early on," he said. "She was so beaten down when I encountered her in the hallway that first Sunday. So were those poor, sweet kids. It looked as if nothing would ever be right again in her life."

By week's end, her transformation amazed him.

"She could have been the queen mother of England, escorting a young prince and princess," Jorgenson recalled. "Her bearing was upright. Her walk was steady and confident. Her face glowed with life. She'd been given a chance for a better life. She had hope. That's what the program was all about, and it was working for people."

Successes such as that prompted Jorgenson to move River Park into a host of new programs, all aimed at expanding understanding of alcoholism and convincing both alcoholics and family members that there was hope. No matter how impossible things seemed, no matter how bleak the situation, there was hope.

That was a message he never grew tired of carrying.

Chapter Eleven

Reaching Out

As River Park worked with more and more alcoholics and their families, Jorgenson became convinced that chances for recovery could be vastly improved if the disease could be diagnosed and arrested earlier, before its progression had done so much damage to the individual and the people around him.

To get the help to an alcoholic sooner meant rethinking one of the traditional beliefs in the field, both among members of Alcoholics Anonymous and in treatment programs across much of the country. An alcoholic or addict, it was widely believed, would come to treatment only when he or she "hit bottom." That is, until an alcoholic had absolutely no other choice, he or she wouldn't willingly accept treatment or do the things necessary to begin recovery.

It isn't difficult to see where that line of reasoning originated. After all, in the early days of Alcoholics Anonymous, most of the people who stumbled through the doors of a meeting hall had lost everything—and many had lost everything several times.

They'd been fired from jobs; they'd quit jobs in a drunken rage or a paranoid craze. They'd been jailed for public intoxication, bar brawls, driving drunk, bouncing checks, petty theft, even felonies. They'd been divorced or separated from their spouses, locked out of the house, forbidden to see the children. They'd been hospitalized for an amazing variety of physical and mental reasons, ranging from cracked ribs after a bar fight or broken bones in a traffic accident to bleeding stomachs from abuse of alcohol and complete loss of contact with reality because of withdrawal.

When they arrived at AA or in treatment, these people, they came as a last resort. They literally had no place else to go. They had hit bottom

Those were the kinds of alcoholics who turned up on River Park's doorstep in its early years. Jorgenson believed that the program the center offered could help each of them, although even his faith was tested a bit by one truly severe case that happened not so many months after treatment began.

A highly successful businessman from the eastern part of South Dakota came to River Park seeking help. He'd been raised in a prominent family, and his business acumen had been exceptional, for he had built quite a strong corporation in his early adult years. In later years, however, he'd turned more and more to the bottle.

By the time he reached River Park, most people had given up on him. There appeared to be no chance in the world that he could sober up long enough to comprehend the message of recovery. How could such a person be expected to even recognize that Step One described him, much less make the decisions necessary to get started on the River Park program?

The man had the emaciated body of someone whose need to drink overwhelmed any desire to eat regular, balanced meals or to observe even the most rudimentary healthy diet practices. His mind wandered, sometimes in mid-sentence. His clothes were filthy and hung like rags on his bony shoulders and torso. His attitude was terrible, too. In his home community, among his friends and family, he'd become known as such an obnoxious fellow that no one wanted anything to do with him.

To top it all off, he'd developed an unappealing skin disease. His hands, face and legs were covered with crusty scales.

"He was the most horrible, ugly sight, and a falling-down drunk as well," Jorgenson recalled.

This client would test everything River Park stood for, but Jorgenson determined that he should have the same chance to become sober that every other alcoholic at River Park received.

"When that man walked in here, if one of the patients or staff had turned away, he would have died," Jorgenson said later.

That didn't happen.

The new client received the same attention and consideration other alcoholics had come to know from the staff and other clients. He was accepted as a person with a fatal disease, and he responded. The man became sober, threw himself into the program of recovery and returned to his hometown to rebuild his neglected business and begin the long task of repairing many, many relationships he'd damaged during his drinking years.

"People in his community couldn't believe the change in this person," Jorgenson said.

That man symbolized the alcoholic who had truly hit bottom, and his recovery helped show how effective treatment based on the River Park philosophy could be.

But pleased as he was for the man's success, it still bothered Jorgenson that he and so many other alcoholics had to endure so much suffering and so much loss before they received help. As River Park and some other forward-looking treatment centers across the country continued to have success in starting even some of these seemingly hopeless drunks on their way to sobriety, Jorgenson and a few other leaders in the field began to question why the process couldn't begin sooner in the course of the disease.

In some ways, this extended the process of public awareness. The more people knew of the signs and symptoms of alcoholism, the more likely they were to recognize addiction in themselves or in someone they loved. But recognizing the problem and admitting it by asking for help were worlds apart sometimes, and Jorgenson began to study ways to push those two worlds closer together.

From River Park's experience by this time, Jorgenson could see that it was possible to move an individual to an acceptance of their alcoholism. Many of the people who had come through the doors started treatment at least reluctant to admit they had a drinking problem. Those people weren't beaten and battered. They were led to the reality of their disease.

Most of those clients, of course, had few alibis. Their excuses had been stripped away by their actions and behavior. But if such people could be brought to an understanding and acceptance of alcoholism, why couldn't others be brought to the same place before they'd lost quite so much?

Why, in other words, couldn't a way be found to raise the bottom? An alcoholic might have to hit bottom before he or she became willing to go to any lengths to become sober. But maybe the bottom needn't be so far down.

How many lives might be saved and how much heartache avoided if the progression of the disease of alcoholism were arrested sooner? It was impossible to say for sure. Clearly, though, it made both human and economic sense to try to help people avoid the worst experiences of alcoholism if that were possible.

That seemed as obvious to Jorgenson as the changes wrought in the field of cancer treatment, for example. New diagnostic techniques and earlier detection of malignant cells saved countless lives. Everybody accepted that. Breast cancer, detected early, could be treated with far fewer side effects than the same cancer that went untreated until it had spread to the entire body. The same was true for prostate cancer, skin cancer, so many other types of malignancies. That's why the healthcare world pushed so aggressively for regular check-ups, routine screenings, and all the things that might make it possible to find and treat cancer before it had done too much damage.

Some experts in the field, as well as many recovering alcoholics, suggested that early involvement was futile. They'd tried to work with other drunks who hadn't lost everything. Far too often, the results were discouraging. The alcoholic sometimes became so angry he tossed his would-be savior out of the house. Or, he might listen intently, agree to think about it, then avoid the "twelfth-stepper" like the plague and continue to drink.

The reason, the skeptics said, was that he hadn't lost so much that his only choice was to quit drinking. He probably still enjoyed his drinking experiences. Time spent on such a person would be wasted. He wasn't ready to surrender, those people told Jorgenson.

Jorgenson listened to them, but he couldn't agree. The more he thought about it, the more he became confident that some principle of early detection should be part of River Park's treatment program. Talking with directors and counselors at other treatment centers across the nation, he began to think about the technique of intervention, a sometimes controversial way to motivate an alcoholic to look at the symptoms and effects of his illness.

When Betty Ford told her story for the *It's Great To Be Alive* program, she spoke of the intervention that forced her to see what her drinking had done to her, to her family and to the relationships they shared. The intervention didn't force her to stop drinking. It did force her to make a decision.

When her daughter, Susan, said she was afraid to leave the grandchildren with Mrs. Ford when she was drinking, she wasn't being mean or trying to hurt her mother. She was simply saying she wanted those children to have a relationship with their grandmother, but she couldn't allow it if the drinking didn't stop. That forced Betty Ford to make a choice. Did she want to continue to have a relationship with those grandchildren? If she did, she needed to take steps to stop drinking. She chose treatment.

But Betty Ford hadn't gone through treatment by the time River Park was beginning its intervention program. This was a wholly new venture, and the nay-sayers came out in force.

An alcoholic can't be forced to quit drinking, they said. How many times had drunks been forced to quit temporarily—because of a stretch in jail, a DWI or whatever? Look at how many of them were unable to stay on the wagon for long. You can't make people quit drinking. They must choose to quit, and even then, it's no easy road to sobriety. That's what the critics of intervention said. And, of course, they were correct in what they said. They just didn't understand the thrust of intervention.

Of course an alcoholic can't be forced to quit drinking forever. An addict can't be forced against his will to get straight. But each can be forced into a situation in which he or she must confront the reality of the drinking or drug use.

In one of his filmed talks on alcoholism, Father Joseph Martin explained the philosophy behind intervention by likening the arguments against it to that old saying, "You can lead a horse to water, but you can't make him drink."

That's all too true, Father Martin said. But, he added, you can let him see the water, and you can make him thirsty.

That's what intervention tried to do. Show the alcoholic the effects of his drinking, offer him a vision of sobriety and make him long to have that kind of life.

The individual didn't lose the power of choice. He could decide whether to try the life being offered or continue on the path his life had been traveling. But through the process of intervention, he'd gain a better awareness of what his drinking had been doing and what the consequences of his decision to continue or to change would be.

Intervention brought many changes to the River Park program.

Staff members had to be trained to facilitate the process. If it sounds as if the intervention technique consisted simply of a bunch of people gathering in a room to tell the alcoholic how miserable he'd made their lives, then that's a skewed snapshot of what happened in such sessions.

Intervention required a good deal of advanced planning and preparation. The counselor met with key individuals in the alcoholic's life, often the spouse, a parent, children, a particularly close friend or clergy member, if possible a supervisor or boss. The supervisor—if willing to be involved and of an understanding nature—often became the key figure in the process. A job was often the alcoholic's last refuge against the admission of a problem. If he could get up and go to work every day, if he could pull his own weight at the office, how could he be an alcoholic? That's what so many problem drinkers fell back on in the end. And if the supervisor or boss were in a position to say, "Yes, your drinking has caused us problems, cost us contracts, forced other workers to cover for you," that sometimes was a more powerful message than any the spouse or children could offer.

It was especially powerful if accompanied by a message of clear choice: If the alcoholic worker recognized and accepted his problem and made the effort to get sober, the company would stand by him and a job would be waiting. If, on the other hand, the alcoholic refused treatment, the company would have no alternative but to let him go.

That's no choice, some alcoholics cried. But it was. The decision was theirs. It may have been a difficult choice, a hard decision. But it was a decision. And it was theirs to make. No one could cover for them; no one could pick up the slack.

Sometimes the intervention process required a spouse to say the same thing. Stop drinking, go to treatment, and we'll try to work things out. Choose to continue drinking, and I can't live with you. Hard words, sure. A tough decision for the alcoholic.

But as Jorgenson had learned in working with the family program, it was a difficult decision for the spouse, too. It isn't easy to tell a husband or wife, "Do this or else." It wasn't easy for Susan Ford to tell her mother the grandchildren might not be able to visit. As Betty explained on the television show, Susan was able to do it only because she cared about her children and her mother. And she'd been prepared to offer that choice as part of the intervention.

When the counselor met with the significant people in an alcoholic's life to prepare for the intervention, it was explained that each person needed to keep examples and comments specific and non-judgmental. The family members weren't to hash over old wounds in a blaming way. If the father had stayed in a bar too long, missed his daughter's high-school graduation and hurt her deeply on that important day, she was to say that in a loving way. The intent wasn't to make the alcoholic feel terrible. If he recalled the incident at all, he probably felt awful each time he relived it. The intent was only to say: "This is something specific that happened to me because of your drinking. Here's how it made me feel."

Without a trained counselor or other neutral party in the room, interventions ran the risk of becoming incredibly emotional, often worthless affairs. Gather the family together to talk about examples of Mom's drinking, and without guidance, the meeting rather quickly could degenerate into a free-for-all. A counselor kept the conversation on point, the process on task.

River Park's experience with intervention was that, in most cases, the alcoholic started the session with a chip on his shoulder. And why wouldn't he? Out of the blue, the people who mattered most to him were gathered to tell him all the things he'd done that hurt them. More than that, they were suggesting to him that if he wanted to change that picture, he must make a decision to seek treatment and stop drinking.

In many instances, this information was coming at the alcoholic months, even years, before the normal progression of his disease would have beaten him down far enough so that he would have been willing to look at the cause and effects of drinking without the help of intervention. So, his emotions often ran wild.

He felt betrayed. How could they sneak up on me like this?

He felt shame. I didn't realize this. How could I have done these things to the people I love?

He felt threatened. How am I going to go back to work with my boss knowing all these things about me?

And, nearly always, he felt fear. How will I get along without drinking?

In some instances the intervention wrought an immediate change in attitude. Faced with the direct and concrete evidence of how the drinking had affected the people around him, the alcoholic made a decision to seek the help that was being offered.

In a good number of cases, though, the intervention produced what might be described as a half-hearted decision. And why wouldn't it? These people were interrupting the progression of a disease before it had fully run its course. The alcoholic might be agreeing to treatment, all right. After all, the job or the family depended on it. But the decision might be taken with a couple of fingers crossed, a sort of unspoken, "Well, sure, I did some crazy things while I was drinking. Who doesn't? But I really wasn't *that* bad, was I?"

The surprising thing, as River Park's staff learned, was that even such a half-hearted decision often turned out to be one that put the alcoholic on the path to recovery. He or she might have gone into treatment to "get folks off my back," or to "show the boss I'm serious about straightening out my life." Even in such lukewarm instances, somewhere inside the doors of River Park, awareness came to the individual.

It required the River Park approach—respect, care and love.

"We'd kind of gotten used to working with alcoholics who were truly desperate to change their lives," Jorgenson said. "Now, we were receiving people who hadn't necessarily lost everything, who perhaps didn't have that vast, horrible drinking past to make them understand that they were alcoholic. We had to approach them in a slightly different way, to let them see what alcoholism actually is, that it's not how much you drink or how often. It's what it does to your life."

Jorgenson and his staff relied on a simple example of alcoholism in dealing especially with some of what came to be known as "high-bottom drunks," the men, women and teen-agers whose drinking progression had been arrested at an early stage. The example River Park used involved trouble.

"If there's trouble in your life—trouble with your wife or husband, trouble with the children, trouble on the job, trouble with the law, whatever—and alcohol is involved, then you could be an alcoholic," Jorgenson and his counselors would tell people.

Notice they wouldn't say, "You *are* an alcoholic." That decision, that step, was up to the individual. During his or her time at River Park, the individual likely would meet and talk with someone whose drinking patterns mirrored his own. Such a meeting inevitably raised in the individual's mind this question: "If he's an alcoholic, and he drank just as I have been drinking, what does that say about me? Perhaps I need to learn more, perhaps I need to examine my own drinking patterns and behaviors."

Those high-bottom folks, the ones unsure whether they really had a problem, sometimes found that others in treatment met their protestations with a friendly if amused tolerance.

"I don't know if I belong here," these doubters would say during a lull in the conversation in the coffee room.

Several of the veterans would smile and nod their heads, as if to say, Yes, we've been in that position, too.

Aloud, one might tell the newcomer, "Well, don't worry about that for a while. Just keep reading and listening, and you'll learn enough about yourself to decide if this is the place for you. It works for a lot of us."

"But this seems to me to be all just a really big mistake," the doubter might say. "I had to come here, or my boss was going to fire me."

"Your boss was going to fire you?" the veteran would reply. "Imagine that. Did he suggest your work wasn't up to snuff? Did he say drinking had anything to do with it?"

"Well," the other might concede, "Yes, I guess there was some talk that my drinking had caused problems, like the time I was supposed to close that big public-relations account and got there late because I'd been drinking. We lost the account, but the PR firm's manager was a real jerk."

"Maybe he wouldn't have been such a jerk if you'd arrived on time and sober," the veteran might answer. "Maybe not, too. It isn't for me to say. But it sounds like that was a problem caused by drinking. It can't hurt you to stick around and learn more about sobriety, can it?"

That kind of simple, common-sense advice, delivered in a friendly, non-judgmental manner by both clients and staff, often was enough to convince the skeptic to set aside his doubts for 30 days and focus on the information and experiences River Park had to offer. More likely than not, after not so very many days of listening and reading and sharing with others, the doubter would find that he was, indeed, powerless over alcohol and that his life—high-bottom and all—had become unmanageable.

The business of handling the high-bottom drunks became invaluable as more and more young alcoholics and drug users began arriving at River Park. Some were court-ordered after a drinking and driving offense or a series of incidents involving marijuana. Others were there because of an intervention approach through their school or church or a River Park outreach program.

The younger the person, the more difficult it sometimes seemed to find life-destroying experiences that would show them how devastating their drug or alcohol use was becoming.

A River Park counselor who worked with many of the young people in those days put it this way: "You can't always just show them a tape of their life and say, here's how low you've sunk. They haven't lived long enough to have that succession of horrible experiences that makes it impossible for an older person to deny the problem. With young people, the approach had to be relatively soft, a question of whether their drug or alcohol use was interfering with the goals they have and the dreams they hold."

If, for example, a young runner got stoned after school instead of going to track practice, wasn't that interfering with his goal of running a state-qualifying time in the half mile? Those were the kinds of questions the counselors would ask their young clients to consider. The approach took considerable time and patience, but it proved to have a high rate of success with the young people who came through River Park.

One of the reasons it worked was that River Park didn't lose sight of the basic addiction problem facing young people. While newspaper and magazine articles talked then and continue to talk about speed and meth and crack cocaine and marijuana, it remained true that, for most teen-agers, the drug that gave them problems was alcohol. It was readily available, too often seen as harmless by the young people and a sort of "rite of passage" by adults, and it got them intoxicated.

And when River Park counselors talked with young people about drug and alcohol use, they made sure to step out from behind the pulpit. Here's what a basic brochure from the treatment center from 1981 said about the approach:

"We've learned at River Park that sermons and horror stories don't make it with young people. They won't be scared or lectured out of using alcohol and other drugs. But they can be shown the consequences of their actions in a concerned and caring way that convinces them someone does understand their feelings and is ready to help with the special problems of growing up."

That approach succeeded.

And, while every successful outcome at River Park was cause for celebration, the teen-agers who found sobriety brought a special joy to the hearts of Jorgenson and his staff. A person whose drug or alcohol abuse was arrested at 18 instead of 48 had avoided 30 years of sorrow for himself and for those whose lives he touched.

So when teen-agers began the program of recovery and returned to their schools and homes and communities carrying that message, they touched other teen-agers. The message of hope got spread to a younger and younger crowd. Whether or not that would result immediately in more young people turning from destructive drug and alcohol use, it was certain that in the long term, these young people would influence countless thousands of others. Perhaps over time, the sober teens would even influence their generation enough so that it would avoid the long, painful and sometimes fatal journey through alcoholism and recovery the generations before them had had to take.

The possibility that alcoholism could be, if not erased completely, then at least limited in future generations by beginning the battle earlier inspired Jorgenson to create a series of school programs.

The pilot program started in the Lead-Deadwood school system in South Dakota's Black Hills. A full-time counselor, hired and paid by River Park but assigned to the Lead-Deadwood school system, spearheaded the project. Picked for his ability to get close to the students, he helped them handle many areas of trouble in their lives. He concentrated, though, on alcohol and drug abuse.

River Park quickly learned that the program could have an impact, both in dealing with students abusing alcohol or other drugs and in helping those students cope with a chemical dependency problem in their family.

"We've learned that often a teacher or counselor is the first to notice personality changes, emotional problems and other signs that accompany a growing chemical addiction or the stress of living with an addiction problem at home," Jorgenson said in a report on the first year of the Lead-Deadwood project.

Using that pilot program as a model, several other school districts in the state created their own drug-alcohol offices. River Park also created a number of outreach offices, designed to be resources for both adults and children with alcoholism questions or problems. Those offices and the treatment center, too, carried a wide array of films, tapes and publications available to schools for drug-alcohol programs. And, as Jorgenson had been doing from the earliest days of the treatment center, he and other staff members at River Park were available to speak or lead workshops on issues of chemical dependency.

"Each time you have a young person taking a stand against drug and alcohol use, you increase the chances that others will be able to do the same," Jorgenson said. "It can build on itself."

That's what River Park was doing, too—building on itself.

From a single in-patient treatment center in an unused portion of a convent, the River Park program had blossomed. Its programs of treatment, outreach and awareness reached across state lines into the Upper Midwest region.

Ten years after the first group of clients entered River Park in Pierre, a similar group walked into the corporation's second in-patient facility, River Park of the Black Hills.

Located just north of Rapid City and only a 30-minute drive from the internationally known granite carvings of four U.S. presidents at Mount Rushmore, River Park of the Black Hills lay in a quiet valley ringed by steep hills thick with dark-green pine trees. Like its sister facility in Pierre, the treatment program at River Park of the Black Hills followed the AA principles. A few years later, a third River Park in-patient facility opened, this time in Sioux Falls, the state's largest city and the hub of an economic and marketing area that reached well into Minnesota, Iowa and Nebraska.

The *It's Great To Be Alive* series was being shown on television networks in 14 states, and the list of nationally known alcoholics and children or spouses of alcoholics who made appearances on the program continued to grow. The program caught the attention of *Alcoholism* magazine, which featured River Park's awareness programs in an issue that included a front-page photograph of Ralph Waite and had the "It's Great To Be Alive" slogan emblazoned in headline type across the cover of the magazine.

Also gaining national attention was River Park's employee assistance program. Almost from the beginning, Jorgenson had known that a component of the program focusing on alcoholism in the workplace was essential.

He knew how important a job and an understanding supervisor could be in an alcoholic worker's decision to seek treatment. He also knew that far too many companies in the country were failing to recognize alcoholism in their work force. It cost money to have a practicing alcoholic on the payroll. The alcoholic added to the company's expenses in a hundred ways—lost time on the job due to sickness or hangovers, slipshod work, half-hearted efforts—not to mention an unproductive atmosphere around the office created by the negative attitudes of the alcoholics.

One relatively conservative estimate Jorgenson used when he talked to employers was that it cost a company at least $5,000 a year for each undetected or untreated alcoholic or drug addict on the payroll. That was money that failed to make it to the bottom line, that wasn't going into shareholders' dividends or new product development or employee incentives and salaries.

Jorgenson recalled a time he approached a major Black Hills business to talk about starting an employee assistance program. The company had been in business for most of a century. It had a large workforce, one that Jorgenson knew from national statistics and from personal experience must include a number of chemically dependent men and women.

He made his pitch to the chief executive officer, who nodded, thanked him for an impressive array of facts and figures but then said, "We don't need an EAP program here. We don't have alcoholics on our payroll."

What the CEO didn't have was the knowledge and education it required to recognize alcoholics on the payroll. Too often good workers who became alcoholic were simply fired. As their disease progressed and their work suffered, they were demoted, reprimanded and eventually let go.

"It costs a company money every time a good, experienced worker is lost," Jorgenson said. "The business faces the costs of recruiting, hiring and training another employee, and it faces the expense of lower production until that new worker attains the skill and experience of the previous employee. Any time a company can recognize an alcoholic in its work force and help that person into a successful treatment program, both the company and the individual are money ahead."

River Park developed an employee assistance program for large companies and small, providing education for personnel managers and human relations staffers and working with the company officers and the problem employees to successfully resolve the issues of chemical dependency. The EAP program also included intervention services, and River Park showed that in a job-related setting, that technique was particularly effective.

When *Fortune* magazine did a cover story on drug use in the workplace, a staff writer visited River Park and had long interviews with Jorgenson. They discussed the incidence of addiction and alcoholism in business and the success of EAP programs. The magazine ran portions of the interview in a June, 1985, issue entitled "The Executive Addict."

By now, River Park had been in operation for 15 years. In that time, it had developed a comprehensive program of alcoholism treatment and awareness with a whole-community philosophy.

When Jorgenson started River Park's in-patient program, he often referred to it as a way to treat the whole person. A person who is chemically dependent becomes sick in body, mind, emotions and spirit, he said. To be successful, a program of recovery ought to focus on each of those elements as well. The object was to put the person back together, to make the alcoholic whole again.

That became the object of River Park's multi-faceted work in the field of alcoholism. The whole community needed attention if the disease were to be successfully treated. River Park was now offering education and awareness programs to groups—medical students, nursing students, clergy, teachers and employers. In-patient treatment was essential to arresting the disease in each alcoholic, and family treatment was just as vital for those who lived with an alcoholic. Awareness education, early intervention, aftercare and outreach took the message of hope and the program of recovery throughout the community.

River Park's success spawned many other programs that tried to use the approach Jorgenson and his people developed. Some imitators succeeded, generally because they focused on principles of AA and respect for the individual and family. Others failed, offering a program that only appeared to be the equivalent of River Park's.

River Park approached the end of its second decade of operation with a changing world around it.

Costs of treatment were rising as more groups entered the field. Insurance companies began to balk at paying, not only for some of the aftercare and family services, but also even for some of the basic in-patient programs.

A combination of insurance requirements and state and national accreditations made it more and more difficult for recovering alcoholics—the backbone of the treatment program because of the message they carried—to continue to be recognized as counselors. Often they lacked the psychology or social work or counseling degrees necessary to meet accreditation standards. While they might be most effective in reaching another alcoholic, they didn't have the diplomas and certificates to hang on the walls of their offices.

Taken together, the changes made it more and more difficult for River Park to continue as it had since 1971. In 1988, River Park merged with Parkside, a division of Lutheran General Health System that had treatment centers in several cities. In 1992 Lutheran General closed many of its treatment centers, and the former River Park facilities in Pierre, Rapid City and Sioux Falls were shut down.

Jorgenson, who had maintained control of the River Park Foundation when the treatment centers merged with Parkside, felt a sense of loss when the programs closed.

"It was something unique, really, in the history of alcohol treatment," he said. "But things moved on, and I decided to get back to awareness and education. No matter how much progress we'd made, too many people still failed to understand alcoholism and the alcoholic. I could see that a major effort remained in that area."

And River Park remained the force that could make that effort.

✳ ✳ ✳

Chapter Twelve

New Beginnings

With the perspective of four decades of work in the field of alcoholism, Glenn Jorgenson has mixed feelings about the progress that's been made from the days when every alcoholic was considered a skid-row bum and a mother could say in all sincerity, "My daughter can't be an alcoholic; she was a debutante."

Jorgenson has poured his life into expanding awareness and understanding of alcoholism as a disease that can be treated. Even so, on some of his more pessimistic days, he says, "This may be overstating things, but it's kind of my gut feeling or educated guess that we're pretty close to where we were when I started."

He still sees an incredible number of people who don't understand addiction.

"Too many people still are out there who look at an alcoholic and say, he could quit if only he *would,* when the truth is, he would quit, if only he *could*," Jorgenson said. "It hurts to say that, because so many people have worked so hard to change things. But so many of the developments in the field of addiction treatment since 1970 have been both good and bad."

Insurance companies agreeing to pay the cost of inpatient treatment made help available for more people. At the same time, some programs abused insurance benefits, and the backlash—refusal by the companies to pay claims except in narrowly defined circumstances—probably was inevitable.

The influence of insurance companies and state accreditation led to more structured programs in terms of education and experience of counselors, availability and level of nursing care, and regulation of facilities to meet standards of the accrediting agencies. The knowledge that trained mental health and counseling specialists brought to addiction treatment was a plus, Jorgenson said, but often such people didn't know first-hand what it was like to be an alcoholic or to live with one. A book or a college class didn't provide the same kind of education that life did.

"The whole business of certification pushed a lot of recovering alcoholics who'd been staff members out the door, and many times those were the people who, regardless of whether they had any formal education or not, were able to get through to that new client," Jorgenson said.

Having trained professionals helping certainly isn't against anything the philosophy of AA suggests. The Big Book of that organization recommends using any help that's available. But some programs have rushed to become so professional that AA has been shoved aside.

"You look up and you wonder what they've done with the principles of the Alcoholics Anonymous program," Jorgenson said. "That's what worked best for the most people over the years. It should be the centerpiece of any program."

Intervention has caught on in a number of centers, and many companies have an employee assistance program that includes chemical dependency services, along with mental-health and marriage or personal counseling.

"I guess what I don't see as often as I did when we were starting is the sense of urgency or of crisis that once existed," Jorgenson said. "You don't hear much about alcoholism or addiction these days until somebody drinks himself to death or dies in a car wreck while driving drunk. Society wrings its hands over the drug use by young people, but you can still go into any community and find parents and civic leaders and law enforcement officers who are relieved when they bust a bunch of kids who are having a party that 'just' features beer."

On the positive side, awareness has been raised, he believes.

"When we were starting out, awareness that alcoholism was a disease was absolutely nil," Jorgenson said. "I think we need ongoing, relentless education programs, but I have to be pleased with the fact that companies are trying to save alcoholic employees and with the fact that family treatment is seen as an important part of the mix. We were always convinced those components were essential."

A book by former U.S. Senator George McGovern about his daughter's terrible, decades-long struggle with alcoholism rekindled some of the flame that had been flickering in the battle against the disease, Jorgenson believes.

McGovern, who served 18 years in the Senate as a South Dakota lawmaker and who ran unsuccessfully as the Democrat Party candidate for president in 1972, wrote the story of his daughter, Teresa, who died of alcoholism at the age of 45.

The book *Terry* is a chronicle of Teresa McGovern's thoughts and fears as gleaned from journals and diaries she left behind, At the same time, the book is an outpouring of McGovern's own grief and care for his child. Teresa McGovern wrestled with her alcoholism from her teen years. She entered treatment programs several times but never seemed able to grasp the elusive sobriety she clearly wanted. In 1994, she froze to death in a snow bank in an alley in Madison, Wisconsin. She was alone.

McGovern sat with Jorgenson after he'd finished the book, talking about alcoholism, his daughter and his feelings. The conversations were taped for a show in the *It's Great To Be Alive* series.

"I have to believe that Senator McGovern's writing and the travels and lectures he's done will help keep the issue of chemical dependency alive in the country," Jorgenson said.

That's what Jorgenson is trying to do with the River Park Foundation.

Ever since the River Park treatment centers were merged with Lutheran General Health System in 1988, he's been concentrating on the possibilities the foundation offers for continued education and awareness programs nationwide and for special education efforts targeting young people.

It's almost as if the fight against chemical dependency has taken on a whole new dimension with the foundation's work.

In the beginning, the effort was basic and two-pronged: Get help to alcoholics who suffer. Lessen the social stigma attached to the disease by making more people in the country aware that alcoholism is an illness, not a choice made by bad or weak-willed people.

Beyond that beginning, it became clear that treatment and recovery for the alcoholic was only part of the need—that entire families suffered from chemical dependency and entire families needed help.

From those basic programs, much of the chemical-dependency field emerged—intervention to get to alcoholics and their families before they lost everything, aftercare to maintain the contact and the network of support that started with treatment, an expanded group of television awareness programs, employee assistance and school projects and the rest.

Now, River Park is trying to get a jump on the whole cycle of alcoholism by reaching out to the next generation first. It's the effort someone once described as trying to get upstream and keep people from falling in the river instead of standing downstream and trying to pull them out before they drown.

That means really concentrating on young people. It means programs that don't just tell them about alcoholism and drug addiction, although those are vitally important subjects for high school, junior high, and even grade school students to discuss.

But so are self-esteem and feelings and anger management. Each of those is something young people struggle with. Each can contribute to a decision to use alcohol or other drugs. Each is the kind of thing that can make a young person believe he or she is the only person who feels this way, the only one who experiences this emotion or fights this kind of anger or wants to belong this badly.

Carl Eller, a former all-pro defensive lineman for the Minnesota Vikings, knows what it's like to feel like you're the only kid in the world who's ever had strong feelings and emotions. Eller, who played in four Super Bowls and who was considered by many to be one of the greatest defensive ends of all time, says he began using alcohol and other drugs at the age of 14 or 15. He did it to feel good about himself.

A generation of professional football players who lined up against the most ferocious members of a Viking defense that used to be called the

"Purple People Eaters" would have a difficult time believing this, but Eller says that as a high-school freshman, "I somehow felt very inadequate."

That's a pretty typical feeling for an alcoholic, and it's certainly typical of how teen-agers feel, Jorgenson said. "Young people often have that feeling that they're the only one."

Eller certainly did. Whether it was true in fact, in his mind he believed he didn't fit in with the rest of the gang. Drinking looked like the key that would open the group to him.

"It wasn't that I wanted to drink; it was simply that I wanted to be part of something, to belong to something," Eller said when interviewed for an *It's Great To Be Alive* program. "I didn't know where to go with these feelings I had. I thought there was something wrong with me. When I drank…then I felt okay."

He graduated from alcohol to other drugs, eventually developing an addiction to cocaine that cost him $2,000 a week to maintain.

"What I was running from, I don't know," Eller said when Jorgenson interviewed him.

A successful, well-paid football player, he nonetheless ran into financial difficulty because of his cocaine habit. He estimates that the addiction cost him as much as $3 million. He lost some investments, owed taxes, had businesses fail and nearly destroyed himself, all because he wanted to belong as a child and the only way he knew to make that happen was through chemicals.

He found help after his family told him they were leaving.

"I had just about given up. I didn't think that some professional could help me," Eller said. "But when my family said they were going to leave, I knew I couldn't last long without them."

By the time he sought treatment, he said, "I did not recognize my own self in a mirror."

He recovered and began spreading the message of hope to others. His basic message is something Jorgenson emphasized at River Park from the very first days.

"I thought I was hopeless and destined to continue living that way," Eller said. "People need to know that there is a place to go."

Young people, especially, need to be able to find help long before the first time they're asked to make the choice of whether to drink a beer, smoke a joint, take a pill or try the new drugs that find their way into all the neighborhoods of all the cities and towns in the nation.

One way to help the school-aged children is through an expanded "future generations" program such as the one the River Park Foundation is trying to provide, Jorgenson believes.

"It's gotten so comprehensive when you're trying to deal with young people," he said. "You touch on all sorts of people problems; you have to look at ways to give these kids a better sense of self-acceptance."

Programs offering education on drug and alcohol issues fit into that whole philosophy the way River Park always made its treatment programs fit a whole-person approach. Using that philosophy, awareness of the dangers of AIDS and other sexually transmitted diseases is as much a part of a future generations education effort as is traditional drug and alcohol awareness.

"It's a pretty straight-line equation," Jorgenson said. "The more drinking there is, the more sex there is. Besides the dangers of accidents with an impaired driver or the possibility of these kids becoming alcoholic at an early, vulnerable age, you add to the mix all the dangers of sexually transmitted diseases. We really do have to get ahead of this thing, and it is going to take generations to do that."

River Park has found that the *It's Great To Be Alive* interview with Lakota singer White Eagle is widely accepted among young people. That's important, because White Eagle (who died in 1995) talks not only about his addiction to and recovery from alcoholism but also about his struggle to live with a diagnosis of AIDS.

White Eagle talks about his trials and his joys in such simple and direct words that, even through a videotaped program, he manages to make an instant connection with the young people who watch. For teen-agers trying to find a place where they're accepted, White Eagle is able to tell them they aren't unique in those feelings.

He never felt as if he belonged, not until he began to drink. Then, he said, he could mask the negative feelings, for a while, at least. Young people also connect with White Eagle's explanation of how he used his powerful voice to win acceptance, and how he lived in fear that if he couldn't sing, he couldn't be accepted.

"I was afraid to sing, because if I didn't sing good, I wasn't good," he said.

After his treatment for alcoholism began, White Eagle discovered that he didn't have to sing to be accepted, because he had begun to accept himself. "I don't have to sing any more," he said. "I want to. I like to. But I don't have to."

Each young person who hears that message and makes a step toward self-acceptance is one more success story in the developing battle to save future generations.

Former Minnesota Twins infielder Greg Gagne would agree with that.

"I felt kind of lonely, that nobody really cared about me," Gagne said in describing the process that led him to use alcohol. "But there are people out there who care about you."

Veteran actor and singer Clifton Davis, himself recovering after years of cocaine abuse that plummeted him into such a severe depression he nearly attempted suicide, is adamant that children need to be the focus of future efforts to stop drug and alcohol abuse.

"We have to challenge them to excellence," Davis said in a conversation for the *It's Great To Be Alive* program. "We have to challenge them to live a happier life."

That means adults must set an example in the way they live, he said.

Cheryl Ladd, an actress who starred in the popular *Charlie's Angels* television show, said parents can play a vital role. She didn't use drugs or alcohol when she was growing up in Huron, South Dakota, and she says one of the key reasons is that her parents helped her learn self-esteem.

"My parents gave me a really good sense of responsibility," Ladd said. "It gave me an opportunity to trust myself and to know myself."

Her message to young people facing a decision on whether or not to use drugs would focus on the damage it can do to goals.

"The big negative about alcohol and drugs is that they're great destroyers of dreams," she said. "They take so much away from you."

Young people need more education to understand those kinds of effects, Clifton Davis said. They need to be helped to take a longer view of life while they're still in high school.

"Let them know the future lies beyond prom night," Davis said. "The world doesn't end that night."

Those words could almost be used to describe the thrust of the new River Park Foundation initiatives, a group of programs Jorgenson believes may be the most important work he and River Park have taken on yet.

One such effort is the River Park "Healthy Kids = Healthy Families" project, housed at the South Dakota Hall of Fame center in Chamberlain, South Dakota. The Jorgensons have decided that all profits from the sale of this book will go to the project as well as other continuing River Park Foundation efforts to bring hope and help to people afflicted and affected by alcoholism or other addictions.

"If we can even make a beginning at reaching ahead to that next generation, we've accomplished something truly meaningful," he said.

And as the future generations efforts expand and flourish, new challenges are sure to arise. The work is never finished when that work involves the human condition.

"At every step in River Park's development, I'd pause and think this was really it," Jorgenson said. "Inpatient treatment was an incredible goal. It took tremendous effort and hard work and planning, a little luck and a lot of faith in God. But no sooner had we gotten that up and running well than it became obvious more awareness was needed, and treatment for the families and all the other things that followed."

As he tried to fashion River Park programs to respond to each developing need, Jorgenson said he began to view the process as a series of opportunities to help other people.

"That's what it's been about, from the first inpatient center to the River Park Foundation's forward looking programs," he said. "I know I've benefited far more than any of the people River Park has tried to help.

And, even though I'm beginning to understand that the work will never be completely finished, it truly is great to be alive."

Resources

Consult your local telephone or internet directory to contact the following organizations. Programs and referrals are offered in many communities.

- Alcoholics Anonymous
- Al-Anon
- Alateen
- Narcotics Anonymous
- Gamblers Anonymous

· · ·

The United States Department of Health and Human Services provides a listing of substance abuse treatment facilities on this website:

http://findtreatment.samhsa.gov/TreatmentLocator/
faces/quickSearch.jspx

· · ·

More information about River Park and videos from the
It's Great To Be Alive television series:

http://www.riverparksd.com

Terry Woster grew up on a farm northeast of Reliance in Lyman County, South Dakota. He graduated from Chamberlain High School in 1962 and from South Dakota State University in 1966 with a degree in journalism. The Sioux Falls Argus Leader gave him his first fulltime newspaper job, staff photographer, in 1967. He wrote features and sports at the paper for two years and then took a job with the Associated Press in the wire service's Pierre bureau in 1969. After nine years with the AP, he took a job as managing editor for the Daily Capitol Journal and left that in 1987 to become Capitol reporter for the Argus Leader. He held that position for 22 years, until he retired in December of 2008. He currently works as public information officer for the South Dakota Department of Public Safety. He also freelances for the Mitchell Daily Republic and the Tri-State Neighbor. He married his high-school sweetheart, a registered nurse, Nancy Gust, in 1967. They raised three children and have five granddaughters.

Glenn Jorgenson is the President of the River Park Foundation, an entity that provides education, training and information about alcoholism and chemical dependency and its effects on families. A native of Hayti, South Dakota, he taught school, owned and operated several businesses with his wife Phyllis, and worked in state government. In 1965, he was appointed South Dakota's Director of Employment by Governor Nils Boe. With Pierre businessmen Shanard Burke and Jack Parr, he and Phyllis established River Park's first treatment center for alcoholism and drug dependency in 1971. He was President and CEO of River Park until it merged with Parkside, a division of Lutheran General Health System, in 1988. The River Park treatment facilities were closed by Lutheran General in 1992. Jorgenson served on the South Dakota Commission on Alcoholism and the South Dakota Vocational Education Board of Directors. Jorgenson was inducted into the South Dakota Hall of Fame in 1996. He served on the Hall of Fame's Board of Directors from 2005 through 2011.

In addition to her work with River Park's facilities and programs, **Phyllis Jorgenson** is an accomplished artist. The Jorgensons have two daughters, three grandchildren and two great-grandchildren.